Decodable Stories Takehome Books

Level 2

Columbus, OH

SRAonline.com

SRA

An Open Court Curriculum.

Printed in the United States of America.

Send all inquiries to this address:
SRA/McGraw-Hill
4400 Easton Commons
Columbus, OH 43219-6188

ISBN: 978-0-07-610840-4
MHID: 0-07-610840-6

11 12 13 14 15 QLM 14 13

The McGraw-Hill Companies

Contents

Level 2 Decodable Stories 1–50

About the Decodable Stories Takehome Books.......5–6
Parent Letter.......7

1 Sand, Tan Hats, and a Mat.......9–12
2 Mitts and Hits.......13–16
3 A Contest.......17–20
4 Gwen Must Run.......21–24
5 The Red Star.......25–28
6 No Drinks in Class.......29–32
7 Learning to Swim.......33–36
8 Farm Chores.......37–40
9 Paddle, Duck, Paddle.......41–44
10 Kate's Picnic.......45–52
11 Five Gifts for Mike.......53–60
12 The Mole Zone.......61–68
13 Hope's Cute Music Box.......69–76
14 A Good Life at the Lake.......77–84
15 Edith and Pete.......85–92
16 Just a Phase for Phil.......93–100
17 Be a Wrangler!.......101–108
18 A Good Deed at the Beach.......109–116
19 Hit the Trail.......117–124
20 Meet the Bats.......125–132
21 Granddaddy Spider and the Party.......133–140
22 A Force in the Dirt.......141–148
23 Uncle Gene.......149–156
24 A Green Leaf Print.......157–164

25 Meet the Firefighters 165–172
26 Try My Pie 173–180
27 The Boat Show 181–188
28 Apples Up High 189–196
29 A Stroll on Mule Avenue 197–204
30 The Kitten's Rescue 205–212
31 The Museum 213–220
32 Under the Moon 221–228
33 A Robin's Red Plumes 229–236
34 Drew's True Lesson 237–244
35 Look How Pets Adapt 245–252
36 Mr. Brown Sees the World 253–260
37 A Plant that Acts Like an Animal 261–268
38 *Animal Expert* in Outer Space 269–276
39 The Lion and the Mouse 277–280
40 The Bootmaker's Daughter 281–284
41 Kim and the Wave 285–288
42 How Roy Got a Toy Drum 289–292
43 The Koi at the Dragon Gate 293–296
44 Brave After All 297–300
45 Chinatown in San Francisco 301–304
46 Little Havana in Miami 305–308
47 Little Italy in New York 309–312
48 Polish Communities in Detroit 313–316
49 The Seminole Tribe in South Florida 317–320
50 Communities in Los Angeles 321–324

About the Decodable Stories Takehome Books

The ***SRA Imagine It!*** *Decodable Stories Takehome Books* allow your students to apply their knowledge of phonic elements to read simple, engaging texts. Each story supports instruction in a new phonic element and incorporates elements and words that have been learned earlier.

The students can fold and staple the pages of each *Decodable Story Takehome Book* to make books of their own to keep and read. We suggest that you keep extra sets of the stories in your classroom for the children to reread.

How to Make a Takehome Book

1. Tear out the pages you need.

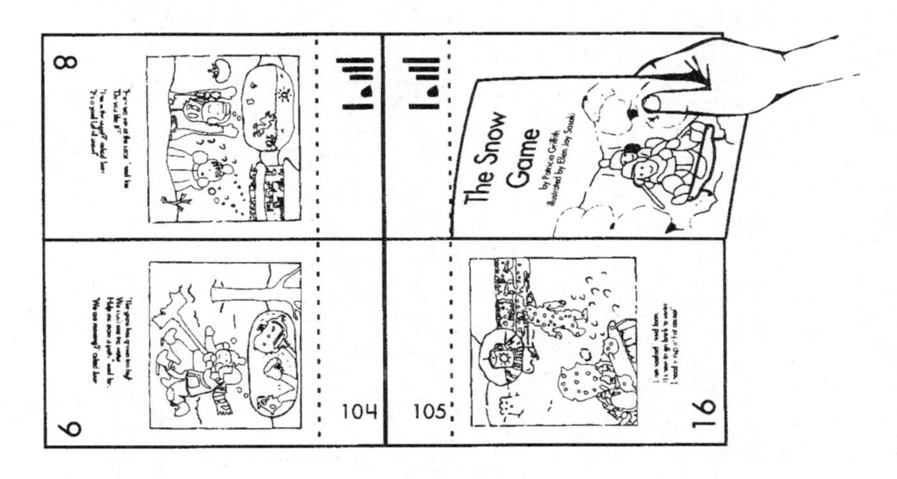

2. Place the title page facedown and the page with two consecutive folios (pages 4–5 in example) faceup.

For 16-page book

3. Place the pages on top of each other in order. The facedown title page will be on the bottom, and the page with the consecutive folios (pages 8–9 in example) will be faceup on the top.

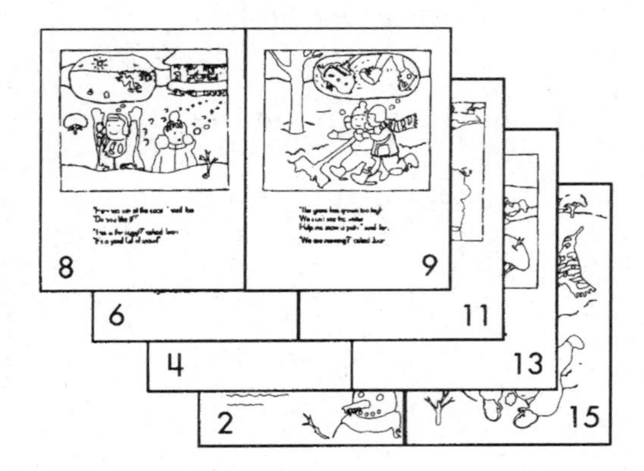

4. Fold along the center line.

5. Check to make sure the pages are in order.

6. Staple the pages along the fold.

For 8-page book

3. Place the page with consecutive folios (page 4–5 in example) on top of the other page.

4. Fold along the center line.

5. Check to make sure the pages are in order.

6. Staple the pages along the fold.

Just to let you know...

A message from ______________________________

Help your child discover the joy of independent reading with ***SRA Imagine It!*** From time to time your child will bring home his or her very own *Decodable Stories Takehome Books* to share with you. With your help, these stories can give your child important reading practice and a joyful shared reading experience.

You may want to set aside a few minutes every evening to read these stories together. Here are some suggestions you may find helpful:

- Do not expect your child to read each story perfectly, but concentrate on sharing the book together.
- Participate by doing some of the reading.
- Talk about the stories as you read, give lots of encouragement, and watch as your child becomes more fluent throughout the year!

Learning to read takes lots of practice. Sharing these stories is one way that your child can gain that valuable practice. Encourage your child to keep the *Decodable Stories Takehome Books* in a special place. This collection will make a library of books that your child can read and reread. Take the time to listen to your child read from his or her library. Just a few moments of shared reading each day can give your child the confidence needed to excel in reading.

Children who read every day come to think of reading as a pleasant, natural part of life. One way to inspire your child to read is to show that reading is an important part of your life by letting him or her see you reading books, magazines, newspapers, or any other materials. Another good way to show that you value reading is to share a *Decodable Story Takehome Book* with your child each day.

Successful reading experiences allow children to be proud of their new-found reading ability. Support your child with interest and enthusiasm about reading. You won't regret it!

SRAonline.com

Printed in the United States of America.

Send all inquiries to this address:
SRA/McGraw-Hill
4400 Easton Commons
Columbus, OH 43219

The McGraw-Hill Companies

Sand, Tan Hats, and a Mat

by Diane Webber
illustrated by Judy Nostrandt

Decodable Story 1

Columbus, OH

Matt, Sam, and Dan sat.
Matt, Sam, and Dan sat at Matt's.

Dan, Sam, and Dad stand and give Matt a hand.

“May I?” said Matt.
“Take these tan hats, sand, and mat,” said Dad.

“I am Matt’s dad. May I help?”

Dad had sand, tan hats, and a mat.

"Matt, stand and give me a hand with these hats."

"Look!" said Sam.

Matt and Dan stand.

SRAonline.com

SRA

Printed in the United States of America.

Send all inquiries to this address:
SRA/McGraw-Hill
4400 Easton Commons
Columbus, OH 43219

The McGraw-Hill Companies

Mitts and Hits

by Daniel Wells
illustrated by Anna Cota Robles

Decodable Story 2

SRA

Columbus, OH

Kim and Bill had been to the Sand Pit before.

Bill and Kim had been to the Sand Pit!

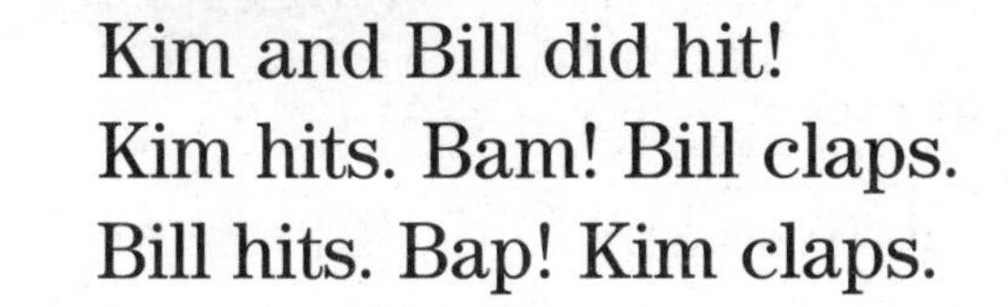

Kim and Bill did hit!
Kim hits. Bam! Bill claps.
Bill hits. Bap! Kim claps.

Bill and Kim stand on a ramp.
Kim had a mitt, and Bill had a mitt.
"Those are our mitts."

Bill had a bat. Kim had a bat.
"Those are our bats."

Did Kim hit? Did Bill hit?
Did Kim miss? Did Bill miss?

SRAonline.com

Printed in the United States of America.

Send all inquiries to this address:
SRA/McGraw-Hill
4400 Easton Commons
Columbus, OH 43219

The McGraw-Hill Companies

A Contest

by Giulia Verzariu
illustrated by Rachel Ivanyi

Decodable Story 3

Columbus, OH

Max is a frog. Max hops off a big log. Next, Max hops off boxes.

"Let's stop to have bread and jam," said Max. Jeff said, "A rest is good for me!"

Max headed fast past a big log.
Jeff hopped past a log and Max!

Max hops past plants. Max hops fast for bread and jam. Max did not stop!

"I hop fast. I am the best. Tell me, who can hop fast?" asked Max.

"I hop fast," Jeff grinned.

"Let's have a contest to tell who is best," said Max.

SRAonline.com

SRA

Printed in the United States of America.

Send all inquiries to this address:
SRA/McGraw-Hill
4400 Easton Commons
Columbus, OH 43219

The McGraw-Hill Companies

Gwen Must Run

by Luke Fisher
illustrated by Karen Tafoya

Decodable Story 4

SRA

Columbus, OH

Gwen gets up at ten.
"I missed the bus!" she yells.

"There is no class," Mr. Buzz tells Gwen.
Gwen tells Mr. Buzz, "Then I did not miss the bus!"

“Can I help?” Mr. Buzz asks.
Gwen tells Mr. Buzz, “It’s past ten, but I cannot get in!”

Gwen runs past her mom.
Gwen tells her mom, “I must run!”

Gwen zigzags past her pal Val.
"Will you jump with us?" asks Val.
"I must run!" yells Gwen.

"Will you stop and visit us?" Mrs. Yip asks.
"I must run!" Gwen tells her. "I cannot quit!"

SRAonline.com

Printed in the United States of America.

Send all inquiries to this address:
SRA/McGraw-Hill
4400 Easton Commons
Columbus, OH 43219

The McGraw-Hill Companies

The Red Star

by Lynn Frankel
illustrated by Judy Nostrandt

Decodable Story 5

Columbus, OH

Mark, Chad, and Trisha sat in the backyard.
"This is not much fun in the dark," said Mark.

"I wish you were smart," Mark said.
"I am smart!" Chad and Trisha yelled.
"But you just wished upon the planet Mars!"

"Which do you wish for?" Chad asked Mark. "Cash or cars?"

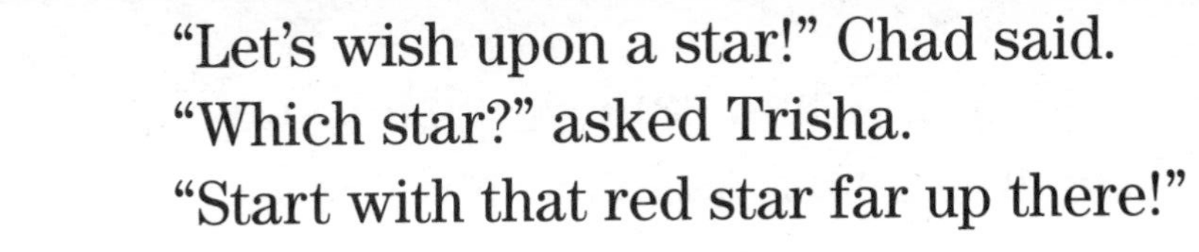

"Let's wish upon a star!" Chad said.
"Which star?" asked Trisha.
"Start with that red star far up there!"

"I will start," Chad said. "I wish to be rich.
I want as much cash as I can get!"

Trisha said, "I want a fast car.
Then I can travel far across the land!"

SRAonline.com

Copyright © 2008 by SRA/McGraw-Hill.

Printed in the United States of America.

Send all inquiries to this address:
SRA/McGraw-Hill
4400 Easton Commons
Columbus, OH 43219

The McGraw-Hill Companies

No Drinks in Class

by Luke Fisher
illustrated by John Edwards

Decodable Story 6

Columbus, OH

It is the end of May. Our class is hot.
It is hard to think.

When the bell rings, I want to sing.
Thank you, bell! Thanks, Mrs. Bridges!

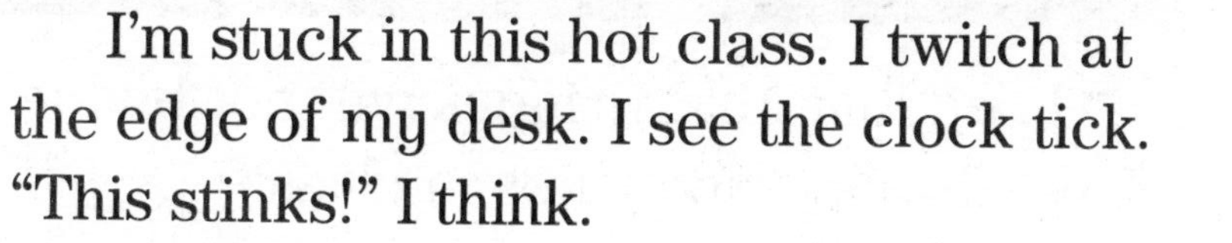

I'm stuck in this hot class. I twitch at the edge of my desk. I see the clock tick. "This stinks!" I think.

Bring me a sprinkler or a bucket of water. I'll splash and have fun.

Pick a dock, and I'll jump off it.

If I were king, I'd sing,
"Bring me six pink drinks!"

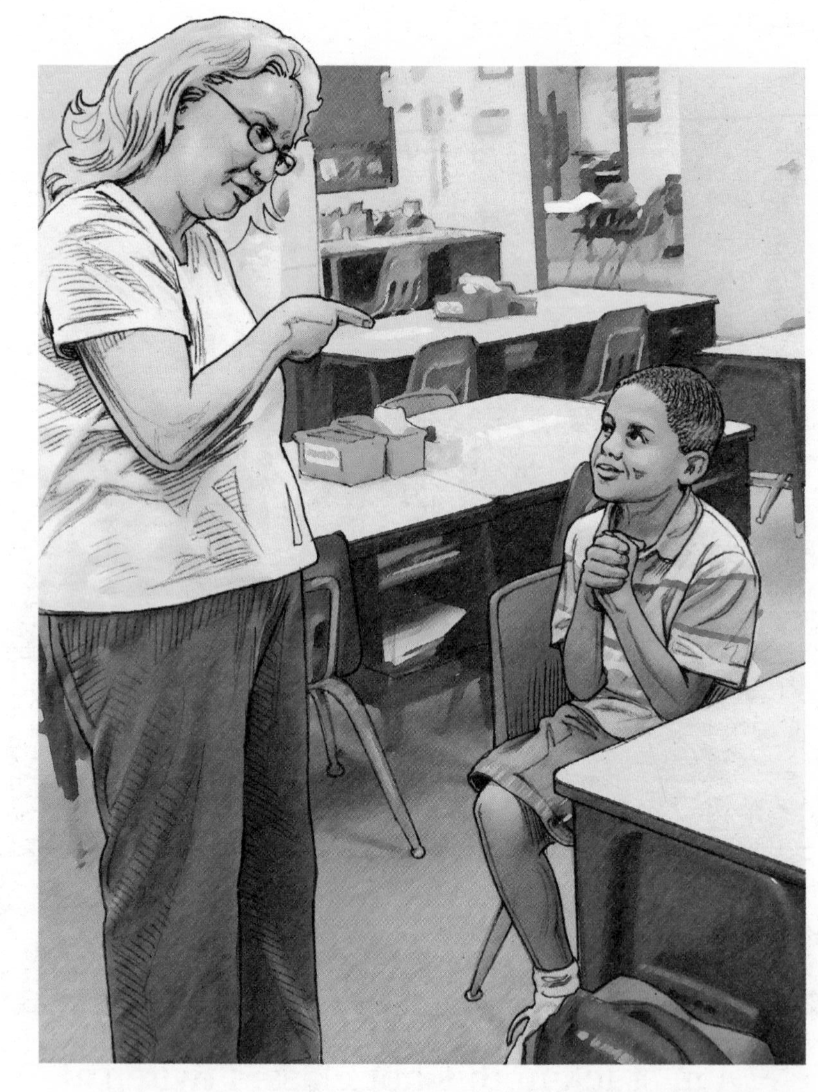

I beg, but Mrs. Bridges will not budge.
She tells me, "No drinks in class!"

SRAonline.com

SRA

Printed in the United States of America.

Send all inquiries to this address:
SRA/McGraw-Hill
4400 Easton Commons
Columbus, OH 43219

The McGraw-Hill Companies

Learning to Swim

by Eileen Breeze
illustrated by John Edwards

Decodable Story 7

SRA

Columbus, OH

“When can I learn to swim, Dad?” asks Burt.
“Let’s start after lunch,” Dad tells Burt.

“Dad, I have never had this much fun!” yells Burt. “And I can still learn to swim much better!”

First Burt stands up. Then Burt jumps!
Burt's head is under the water!

After lunch Dad helps Burt learn to swim.
"Dad, will I get hurt in the water?"
"I will never let you get hurt, Burt."

First Burt puts his legs under the water.
Then his arms are under the water!

Burt is swimming a little better.
“Dad, can I jump in the water?” Burt asks.
“Yes!” grins Dad.

SRAonline.com

SRA

Printed in the United States of America.

Send all inquiries to this address:
SRA/McGraw-Hill
4400 Easton Commons
Columbus, OH 43219

The McGraw-Hill Companies

Farm Chores

by Edward Bricker
illustrated by Karen Tafoya

Decodable Story 8

SRA

Columbus, OH

Dora is a farmer. In the morning she gets up in the dark to do her chores.

Dora grins. Here is the sun!

"I wish one more thing. I wish all days were just like this!"

Dora sits on her horse. “Run fast!” The horse jumps.

“Faster! Faster!” Dora yells. “We must be quick or we will miss the sun getting up!”

“I wish I did not have chores,” she thinks. “But I like to be with the animals.”

"I wish upon that star!" Dora thinks, "No chores!"

Dora brings water for the animals.

"I still have more chores!" Dora mutters. "I must ride the black horse to the store."

SRAonline.com

Printed in the United States of America.

Send all inquiries to this address:
SRA/McGraw-Hill
4400 Easton Commons
Columbus, OH 43219

The McGraw-Hill Companies

Paddle, Duck, Paddle

by Eileen Breeze
illustrated by Stephanie Pershing

Decodable Story 9

Columbus, OH

Ellen is a little duck. She steps past a puddle into the pond.

"I will get a snack," Ellen thinks.

The girl fumbles for bread and tosses it to the little duck.

Ellen gobbles it up and quacks, "Thank you!"

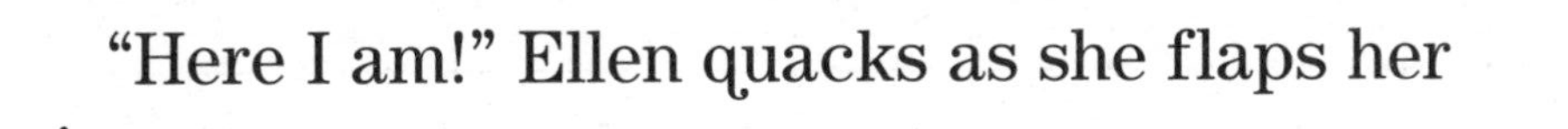

"Here I am!" Ellen quacks as she flaps her wings.

"Look, a little duck!" giggles one of the seven.

"I think you like to gobble bread."

"I will get bread. I will use my head to get bread!"

Ellen paddles to the middle of the pond and spots seven girls on the bank.

"Why, I think they will have bread!"

"I must use these strong legs to paddle!" Ellen puffs.

"Why can't I paddle faster?"

SRAonline.com

SRA

Printed in the United States of America.

Send all inquiries to this address:
SRA/McGraw-Hill
4400 Easton Commons
Columbus, OH 43219

The McGraw-Hill Companies

SRA Decodable Stories

Kate's Picnic

by Sean Saunders
illustrated by Barbara Counseller

Decodable Story 10

SRA

Columbus, OH

Kate and her pals are planning a picnic. The picnic will be in Kate's backyard. Jane and Jan will come.

Kate helped Dad take in things from the yard. "You did a caring thing for Damon," Dad said. "He's just a little kid," said Kate.

After a game, Jan and Jane had to go. Kate and Damon waved. Jan and Jane did the same.

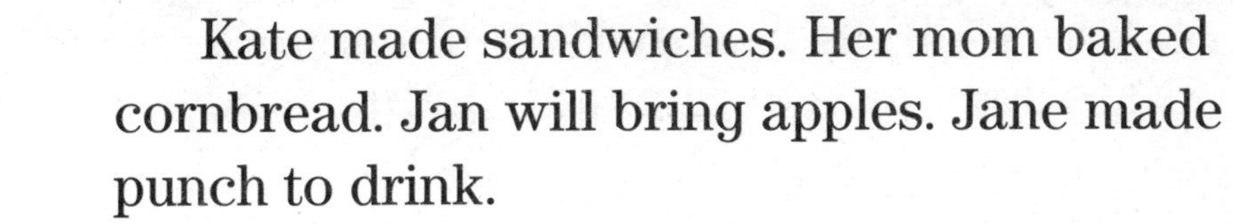

Kate made sandwiches. Her mom baked cornbread. Jan will bring apples. Jane made punch to drink.

Kate set plates on the table in the shade.
Then Jane and Jan came!

"Yes!" said Damon. "I am Picnic Man!
I make the picnic safe!"
Damon and the girls had fun.

Mom came and cut the cornbread.

"Damon, did Kate ask you to her picnic?" Mom asked. She gave Kate a wink.

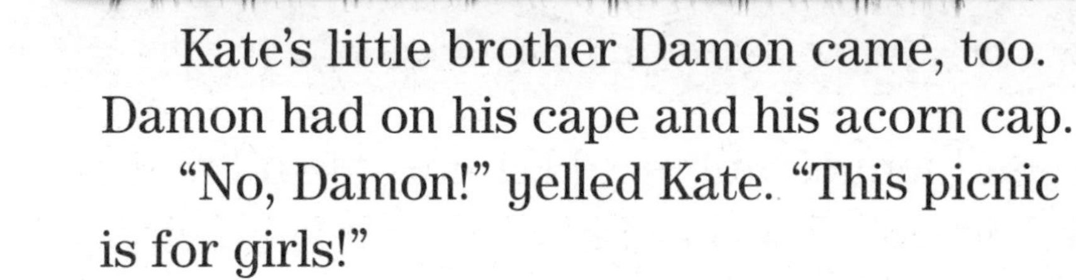

Kate's little brother Damon came, too. Damon had on his cape and his acorn cap.

"No, Damon!" yelled Kate. "This picnic is for girls!"

"I am Picnic Man!" said Damon. "I will make the picnic safe! I want apples! I want sandwiches!"

"Take a sandwich, Damon," said Kate.
"Take an apple," said Jan.
Damon ate and drank a cup of punch.

"I can?" asked Damon. "Thanks!"

Damon gave the girls a big grin. He ran back to the picnic.

"Damon, you are just a little kid," said Kate. "You can't come to this picnic."

Damon felt sad.

"I never get to have fun with Kate," he said. And then he went away.

Jan whispered to Jane. Jane whispered to Kate.

"Come back, Damon!" Jan said. "You can come to the picnic!"

SRAonline.com

Printed in the United States of America.

Send all inquiries to this address:
SRA/McGraw-Hill
4400 Easton Commons
Columbus, OH 43219

The McGraw-Hill Companies

Five Gifts for Mike

by Elizabeth Ramsey
illustrated by Anna Cota-Robles

Decodable Story 11

Columbus, OH

Mike and Kim like to ride bikes. They ride to the park, and Gran rides along.

Kim gives Mike the box of gifts. Gran hands him the card.

"You gave me the park!" Mike grins.

“Mind if I make a card for Mike?” asks Gran. “He likes catfish. I will give him one.”

Kim hides Mike’s gifts in a tin box.

Mike, Kim, and Gran lock the bikes. They like to hike to the pond.

They hike in a line. They hike for a mile. Gran is first and then Kim and then Mike.

Kim and Gran take the gifts to Mike. But first Gran must make a quick stop.

Then Kim finds a big white feather. She gathers a nut, and she picks up a dime. Kim has five gifts that Mike will like.

Five white ducks swim in the pond. The ducks quack and dive. They nibble insects.

Fins make ripples on the pond.
"Which kinds of fish swim in the pond?" asks Mike.

Next Kim finds a little tan shell. These are things that will make Mike smile.

Kim thinks of gifts that Mike will like. She picks up a rock that shines in the sun.

Gran tells Mike, "That kind is a sunfish, and the black fish is a catfish."

"I like the catfish best!" yells Mike.

The fish swam and hid under a rock.

The next time they ride, it is just Kim and Gran. Mike is sick. He must rest in bed.

Kim tells Gran that she misses Mike.
"We can find a gift for Mike," Gran tells Kim.
"Yes!" smiles Kim. "I will find him one!"

SRAonline.com

Printed in the United States of America.

Send all inquiries to this address:
SRA/McGraw-Hill
4400 Easton Commons
Columbus, OH 43219

The McGraw-Hill Companies

The Mole Zone

by Sean Saunders
illustrated by Stephanie Pershing

Decodable Story 12

Columbus, OH

It is a fine morning. The sun is shining. The birds are singing. Dad is going to get the paper.

"The mole *is* little and helpless," Mom admits. "We have space for a mole zone, don't we?"

“Hold on,” Cole chimes in. “The mole broke just two little buds. Old Buster digs holes for his bones, but you don’t give him a cold squirt!”

“This is the best yard on the block,” Dad thinks. “The grass is perfect, and the garden is lush.”

That is when Dad spots the hole. Next to the hole is a dome of dirt.

"No, no," he mutters, "not a mole!"

Mom tells Cole, "Hold this cup while I get the hose! I'll give that mole a cold, wet squirt!"

Mom, in her robe, runs to the open gate.
"Don't let that mole rob my roses," she yells.

"A mole will not stop at a single hole.
This mole must go, and it must go now."

“Mr. Mole, you have got to go now!” Dad yells.
But Mr. Mole is not at home.

“No, no! You two are both no help! You are supposed to chase that mole!”

The mole gets an insect off a rosebud.

Both Bandit and Buster like this thing. Bandit gives it a lick. Old Buster and the mole are nose to nose.

The mole is rolling over the grass. It is headed for the garden!

The mole heads under the gate. Over the hedge jumps Bandit the cat.

"Go, Bandit, Go!" yells Dad. "Get that mole!"

At that, Old Buster the dog wakes up.
"Bark at that mole, Buster!! Send him packing!"
Old Buster trots over and sniffs the mole.

SRAonline.com

Printed in the United States of America.

Send all inquiries to this address:
SRA/McGraw-Hill
4400 Easton Commons
Columbus, OH 43219

The McGraw-Hill Companies

Hope's Cute Music Box

by Margaret Mason
illustrated by Judy Nostrandt

Decodable Story 13

Columbus, OH

This is Hope. She is the best artist in her class. She uses lots of art things in her projects.

Hope shares the art things in her music box. "We can all make better art if we share!"

Hope yells at her sister, "Use the music box, fine! Just ask first next time!"

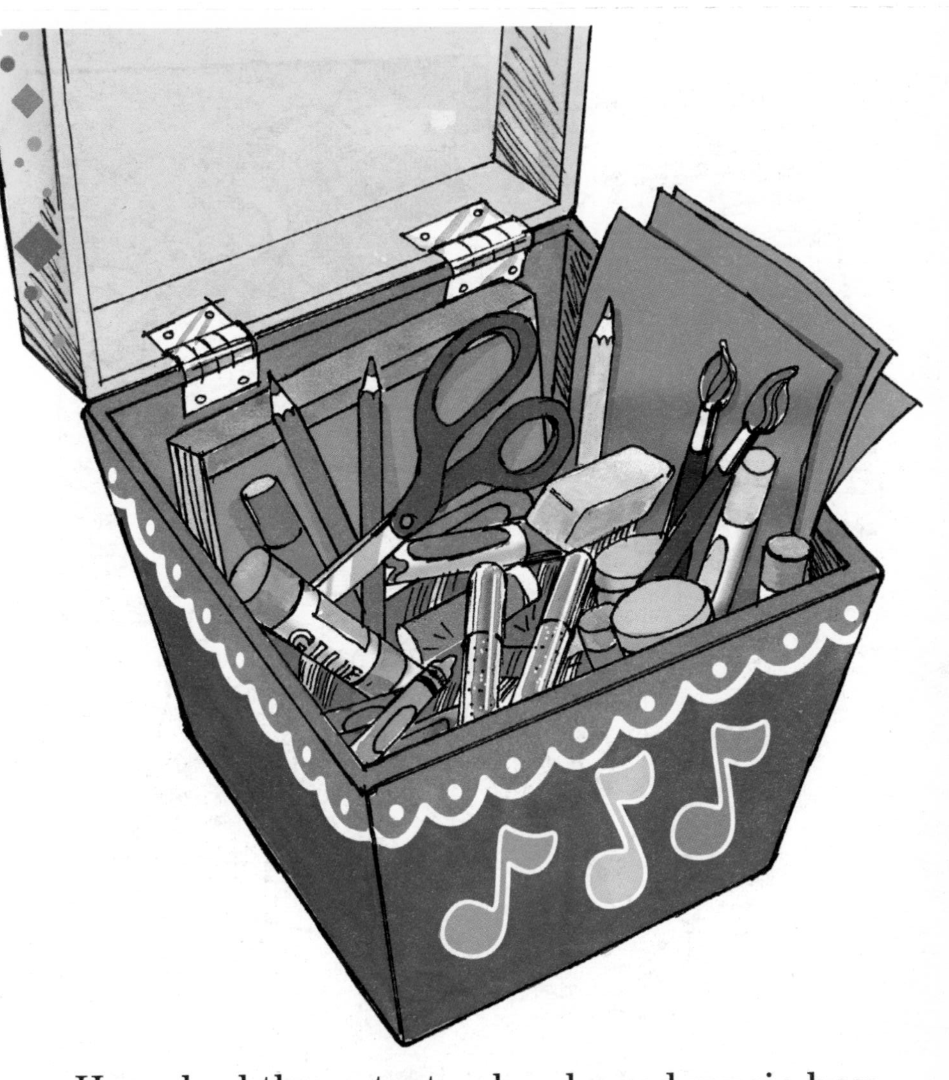

Hope had the cutest cube-shaped music box. She kept her art things in it. But Hope lost her music box.

Hope goes looking for her music box. She finds her lost mule and a human model. Hope cannot find her cute music box.

But Hope is in for a surprise. Her cute cube-shaped box sits on her bed. A note from her sister is on it.

Later, Hope walks home thinking. She will have to buy art things. She cannot afford to buy a cute music box for a while.

It is time for art class. There is no time to buy art things. With no art things, Hope felt useless.

Hope goes to art class and sits at the table.
"You don't have your cute box?" asks Robin.
"Use this paper."
"Thanks!"

The art class starts. Even with no cute music box, Hope makes art. Hope uses her pals' art things.

Simone asks the class, “Can we gather all the pastels?”

The class yells, “Yes! Then we can all use them.”

“Use this, too,” adds Will. “I can tell you like red.”

Hope tells Will, “Thanks! This will be useful.”

Justin lets Hope use his markers. He shares his music, too. Hope likes to make art with music.

Stella sits across from Hope. She hands over glitter and paste.

"You can use this glitter and paste," Stella tells Hope.

SRAonline.com

Printed in the United States of America.

Send all inquiries to this address:
SRA/McGraw-Hill
4400 Easton Commons
Columbus, OH 43219

The McGraw-Hill Companies

A Good Life at the Lake

by Grace Trubiano
illustrated by Stephanie Pershing

Decodable Story 14

Columbus, OH

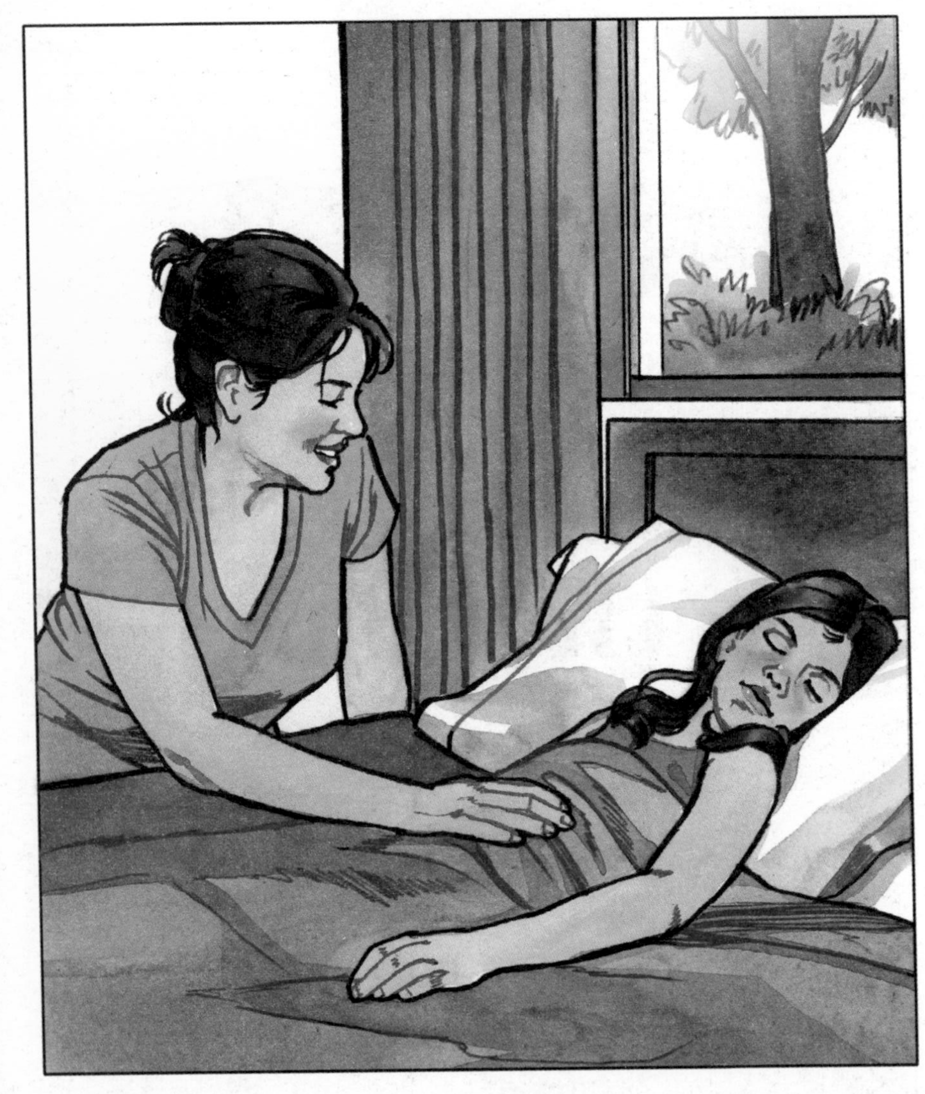

"Rise and shine, Kate!" said Mom. "It is another fine morning! Let's go to the lake and hike."

"Kate!" said Mom.

"Just kidding!" grinned Kate as the fish swam away.

Kate and Mom had a good time at the lake.

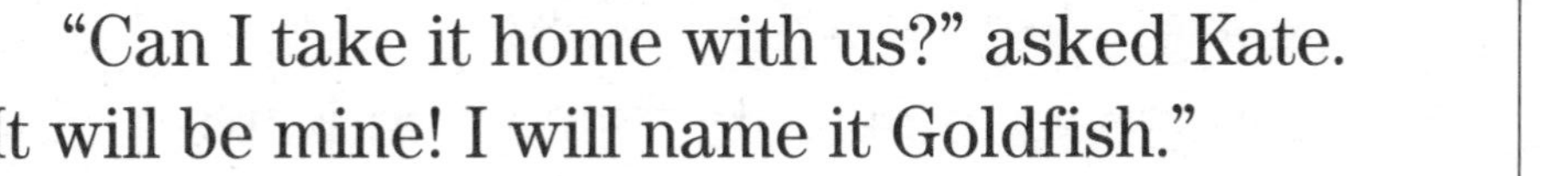

“Can I take it home with us?” asked Kate. “It will be mine! I will name it Goldfish.”

So Kate and her mom went to the lake. They went on a hike. They spotted many plants and animals.

"Look at this, Mom!" said Kate.
"Did you find an animal?" asked Mom.
"I see a cute little frog!" said Kate.

"Look, Mom!" said Kate.
"Look where?" asked Mom.
"I just spotted a cute fish!" said Kate.

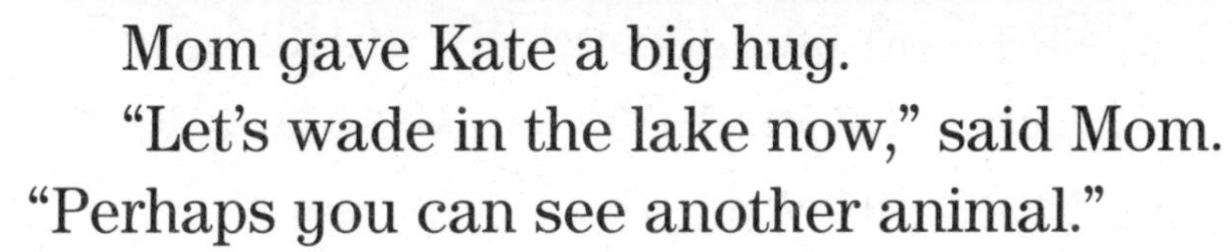

Mom gave Kate a big hug.

"Let's wade in the lake now," said Mom. "Perhaps you can see another animal."

"Can I take it home with us?" asked Kate. "It will be mine. I will name it Spike!"

Just then, the frog ate a bug. And it ate another bug.

"Can you find lots of bugs?" asked Mom.

70

"The frog has a good life at the lake," said Kate. "I don't think it's wise to take the frog home with us."

75

“Not so fine, I suppose,” said Kate.

The frog hopped away. Kate gave a sad little wave.

“Where did the frog go?” asked Mom.

“Yes,” smiled Kate. “I can find many bugs at home in the backyard.”

Kate kept smiling at her mom.

"How will this frog survive at home?" asked Mom.

"I can use a box to make a safe home," said Kate.

"Hold on!" said Mom. "Now the frog has a big lake. Compared to a lake, how is a little box for a home?"

SRAonline.com

Printed in the United States of America.

Send all inquiries to this address:
SRA/McGraw-Hill
4400 Easton Commons
Columbus, OH 43219

The McGraw-Hill Companies

Edith and Pete

retold by Susan Martina
illustrated by Brenda Johnson

Decodable Story 15

Columbus, OH

Edith was taking a stroll on the river bank when she slipped. In the river she went! The water in the river was fast!

Even a little ant can return a kind act. An unplanned kindness does make a difference. We can all be like Edith and Pete!

Did you think Edith would be able to help Pete? What does this tell us? What can we learn from Edith and Pete?

Edith could not compete with the fast water. If she went under, then she would not make it.

Pete saw Edith struggling. Pete was a kind bird. He wanted to help. “How can this be happening?” Pete asked.

Because of these acts, Edith and Pete are both fine. If just one had not helped, this would not be.

Think about the kind acts that Edith and Pete did. Pete helped Edith, and Edith helped Pete.

"I will help that ant," Pete said. Pete got a blade of grass. He dropped it in the river.

"Here!" Pete yelled, "Grab this blade of grass!" Edith got out of the river. Edith was safe.

The cat yelled. This alerted Pete to get away. Now two kind acts were complete. Edith had returned Pete's kindness.

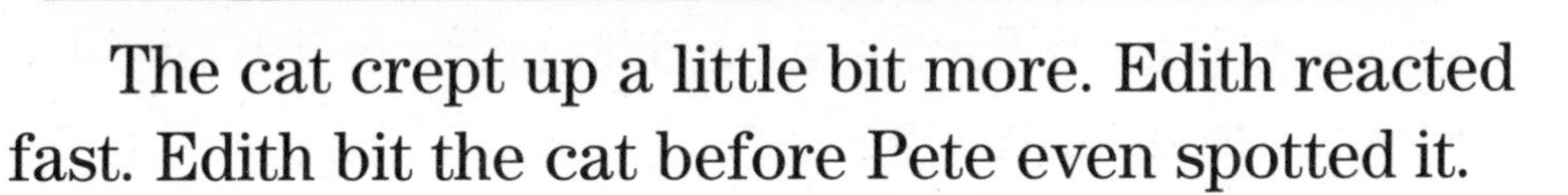

The cat crept up a little bit more. Edith reacted fast. Edith bit the cat before Pete even spotted it.

Pete went over next to Edith. “Are you hurt or sick?” asked Pete. “Do you have a fever?”

"No, I am fine," panted Edith. "Thanks. Because you helped me, I will help you in time."

Later, Edith saw a cat staring at Pete. "This cannot be good for Pete," Edith said. Edith had to help so Pete would be safe.

SRAonline.com

SRA

Printed in the United States of America.

Send all inquiries to this address:
SRA/McGraw-Hill
4400 Easton Commons
Columbus, OH 43219

The McGraw-Hill Companies

Just a Phase for Phil

by Martin Smith
illustrated by Barbara Counseller

Decodable Story 16

SRA

Columbus, OH

Phil had a wreck in here. To get on his bed, Phil had to climb over piles.

"Let me use this comb first," said Phil.
"This is a better phase, Phil!" said his mom.

Tim knocked and came in.

"It looks so good in here!" he said. "Let's take a photo!"

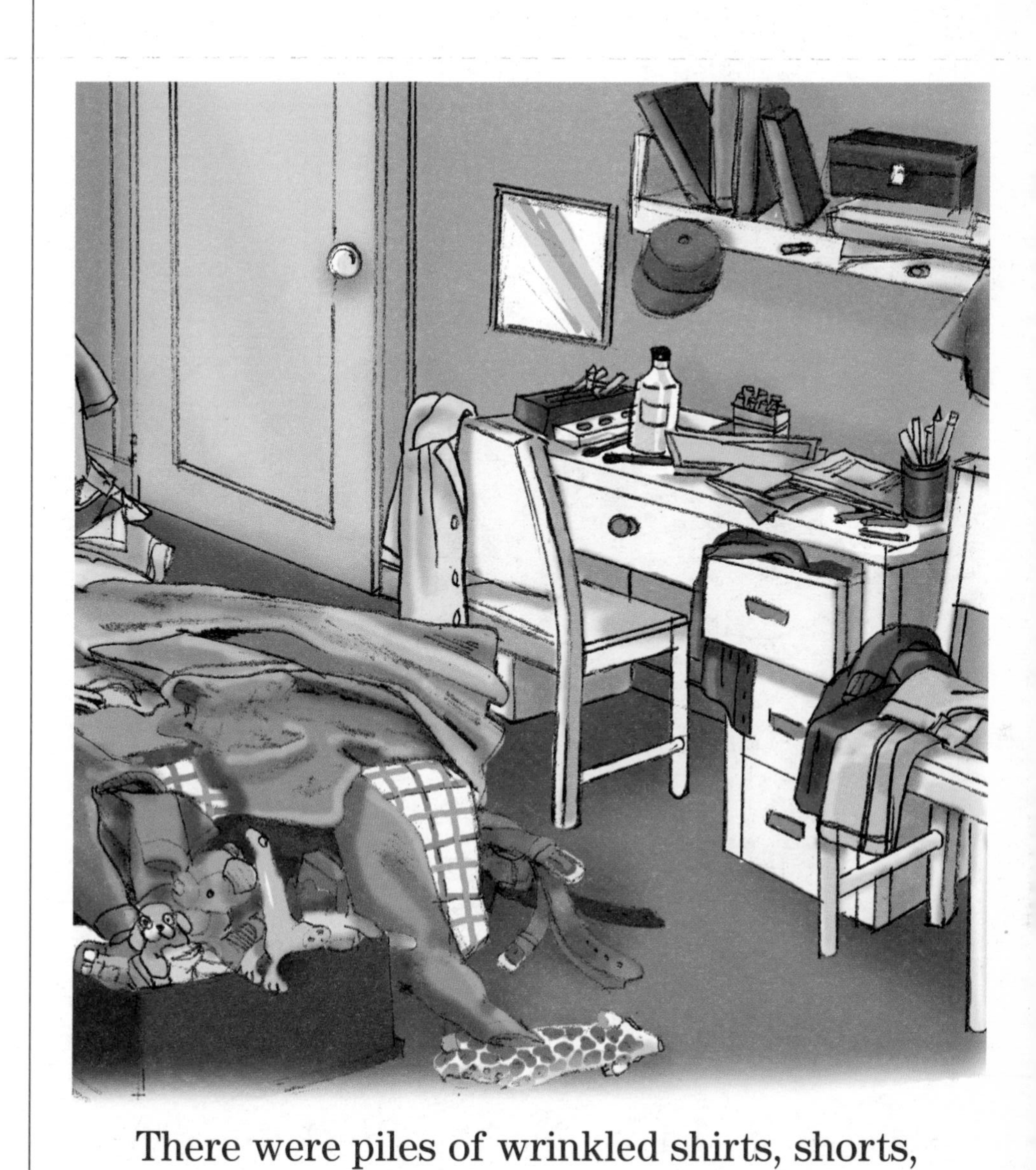

There were piles of wrinkled shirts, shorts, and pants. There were piles of belts with knots in them. There were piles of wrappers and paper.

Phil's mom did not mind the wreck. "People can have a mess for a short time. This is just a phase for Phil," she said.

Phil picked up the wrinkled shirts, shorts, and pants. Phil undid the knots in the belts. Phil picked up the wrappers and papers.

"What is this letter?" Phil asked. "Did a rock star write to me? Did I write to a rock star?"

Phil liked his wreck. He felt he had a knack for making a mess.

Phil liked to win, too. He had a knack for winning! Phil and Tim wanted to have a contest.

"Here is a wrench!" said Phil.

"Did a plumber forget it?" asked Tim.

"I don't know," said Phil. "Here is a phone and a stuffed lamb!"

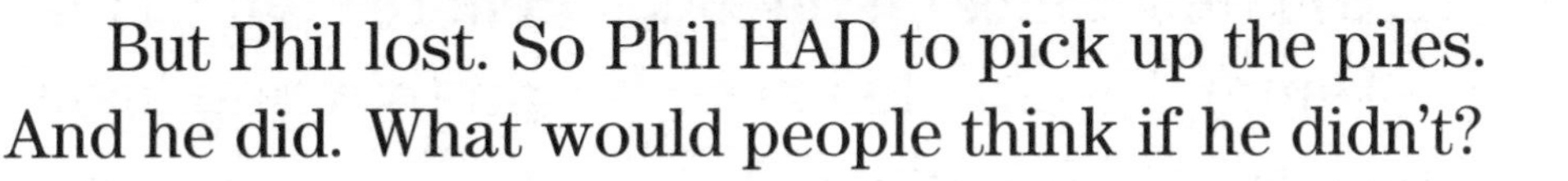

But Phil lost. So Phil HAD to pick up the piles. And he did. What would people think if he didn't?

They grabbed hands and gripped hard. Their knuckles hurt. Their thumbs went numb.

Then Phil's wrist hit the desk. Phil lost.
"You must do what I tell you," said Tim.

"You must pick up the piles in here," said Tim.
"Humph!" said Phil as he began to wring his hands. He did not like this one bit.

SRAonline.com

Printed in the United States of America.

Send all inquiries to this address:
SRA/McGraw-Hill
4400 Easton Commons
Columbus, OH 43219

The McGraw-Hill Companies

Be a Wrangler!

by Martin Smith
illustrated by Karen Tafoya

Decodable Story 17

Columbus, OH

Knock! Knock! Knock! It is a fine morning, saddle pals! Is it your first time here at the ranch?

114

You have a knack for this, partner! We can call you a wrangler now. And it is just the first morning on the ranch!

127

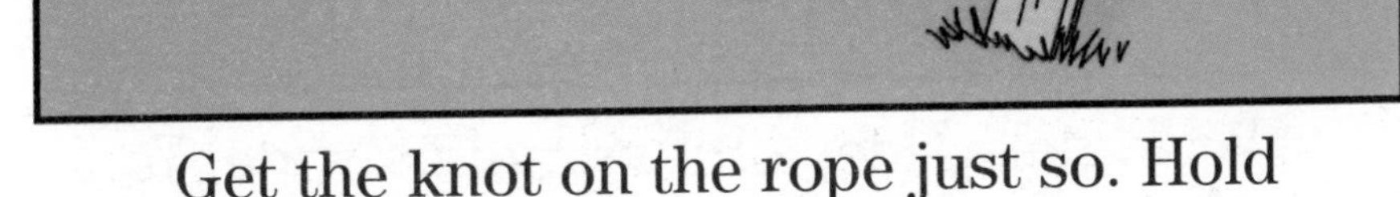

Get the knot on the rope just so. Hold your thumb, swing that arm, and twist that wrist. You can rope!

Are you glad we are here together, partner? We hope you have the best time! Write or phone home to tell your pals all about it!

We offer horse rides here. A ranch visit is not complete until you climb on a horse! Get a horse at the corral, partner.

Wranglers ride, and wranglers rope. You want a rope lesson, partner? Look at the wranglers with the ropes.

Climb off the horse, partner. We can brush Little Lamb, and we can comb her mane. And she will like to nibble on a snack.

These are the wranglers. Wranglers ride, and wranglers rope. The wranglers will find a horse for you to ride.

Here is the finest horse in these parts. Her name is Little Lamb. She has a knack for being charming!

That was a fine ride! You and Little Lamb look good together! Can we get a photograph?

Is the ranch like you hoped it would be? Look out for these limbs, partner! Wrap the rope around your knuckles! Ride on!

Climb up on the horse. The wranglers will help. The wranglers know the ropes.

Check that the knot is set. Step up here and grab the saddle horn, partner. Swing that leg over and climb on.

Ride on, partner! We will ride together with the wranglers. The wranglers go first, and we go behind.

SRAonline.com

Copyright © 2008 by SRA/McGraw-Hill.

Printed in the United States of America.

Send all inquiries to this address:
SRA/McGraw-Hill
4400 Easton Commons
Columbus, OH 43219

The McGraw-Hill Companies

SRA Decodable Stories

A Good Deed at the Beach

by Anna Marie Randolph
illustrated by Barbara Counseller

Decodable Story 18

Columbus, OH

Mom woke us up. “No more sleeping!” she said. “We are going to the beach.”

“Sweet!” we said.

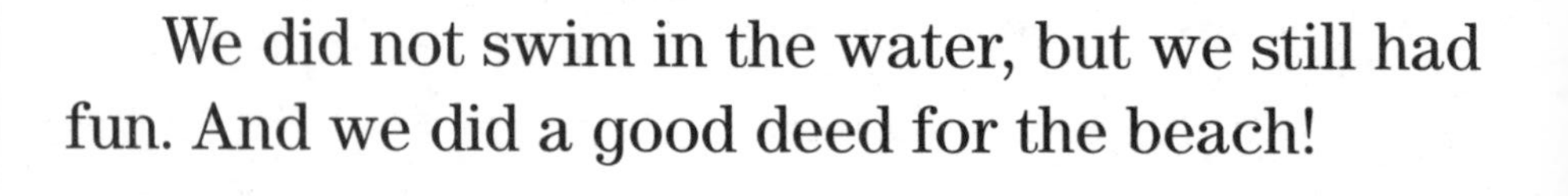

We did not swim in the water, but we still had fun. And we did a good deed for the beach!

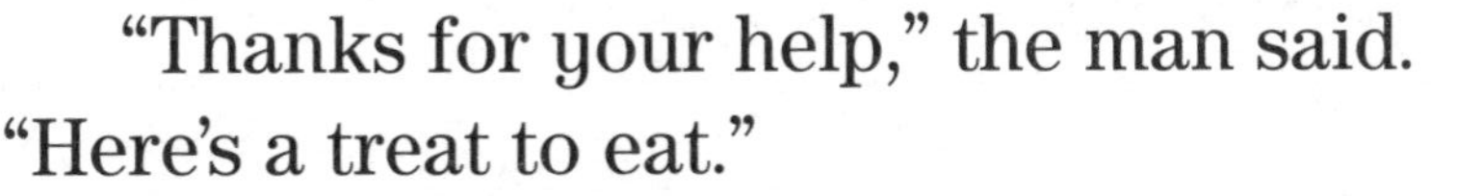

“Thanks for your help,” the man said. “Here’s a treat to eat.”

He gave us a sheet to read. “If you are free, come back in three weeks!”

“Have a bite to eat,” Mom said. “Then put on jeans and sneakers. No swim things this week.”

"What do you mean?" we asked.
"Come and you will see," said Mom.
We got in the car and headed to the beach.

My sister said, "Now the beach is clean! I hope we can keep it neat and clean."

It did not seem to take long. We put all the bags in a big heap. Then we had a seat on the beach.

I could smell the sea. I could feel the breeze. I like to be on the beach.

Then, Mom said, “Read that.”

A poster read, "Clean up your beach. Please help!"

"We need to help," my sister said. I agreed.

My sister picked up a string of beads. I picked up a banana peel.

"At least I have these," I said.

"Sweep the beach!" the man said.
We picked up bags, cans, and more.
Mom picked up a green bottle.

"We will," said Mom. "That is the reason we came to the beach."
We gathered to hear a man speak.

He instructed us, "Pick up trash. But please leave shells, rocks, and seaweed. And keep on the beach! Do not get in the water now."

He told us to clean in teams. The three of us were a team. Each team got a trash bag.

SRAonline.com

Copyright © 2008 by SRA/McGraw-Hill.

Printed in the United States of America.

Send all inquiries to this address:
SRA/McGraw-Hill
4400 Easton Commons
Columbus, OH 43219

The McGraw-Hill Companies

Hit the Trail

by Susan Martina
illustrated by Barbara Counseller

Decodable Story 19

Columbus, OH

It may be a good day for a hike! Here are fun ways to hit the trail. First, let's read tips for safe hiking on the trail.

For example, you may find animals with a tail. Or, you may find things that are gray. You may make a list of them to remember the hike.

Alike Hike

Look for things that are the same in some way. Pick one thing for the day.

Trail Tips

Stay on the trail. It is the best way to be safe. And that way, you do not harm things in the wild.

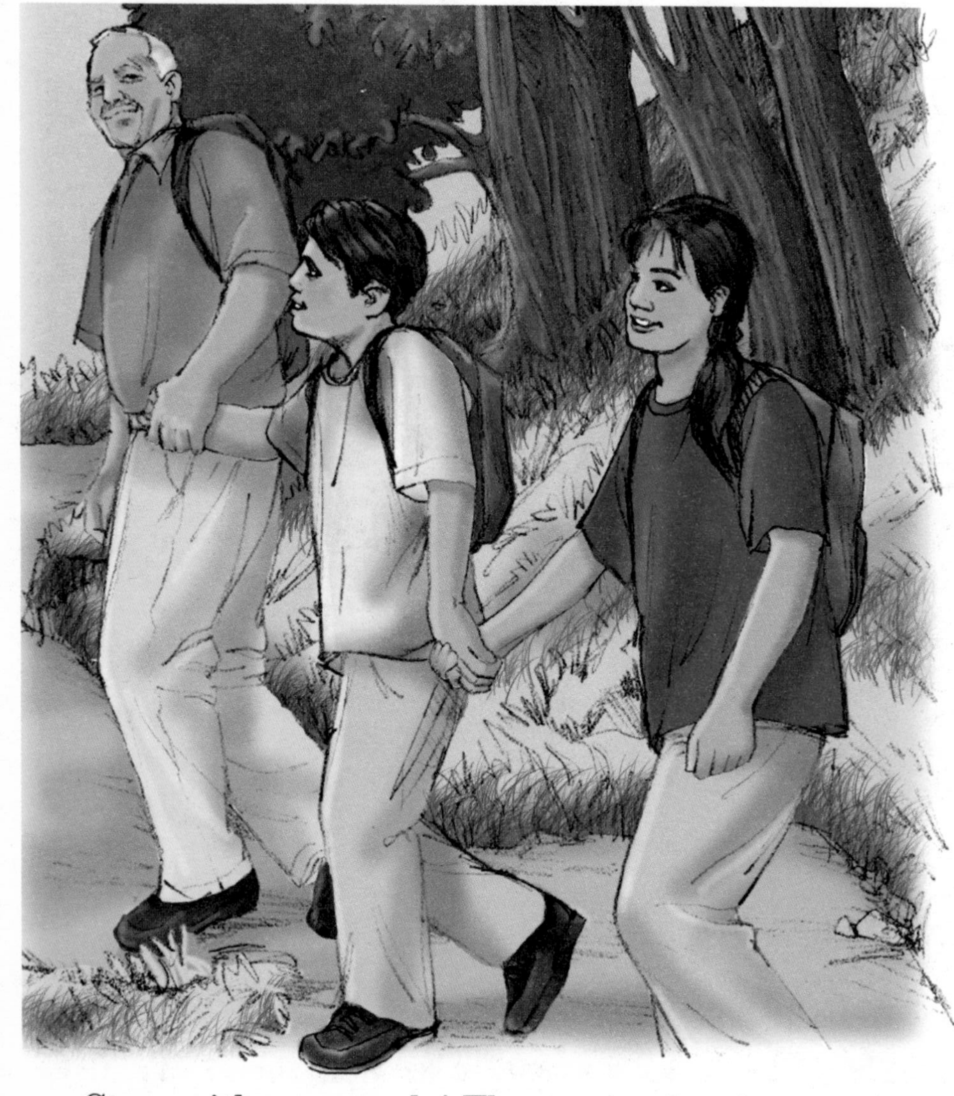

Stay with your pals! There may be times when you want to hold hands and make a chain.

Then find a thing that starts with the letter B and say its name. Keep playing until you get to Z.

A to Z Hike

To play, look for a thing that starts with the letter A. Say the name of the thing.

Take away those things that you bring. But let plants and animals stay right where they are.

Heads or Tails Hike

Can't agree which way to go? The heads or tails hike is best if you like to explore.

Or, you may take clay with you. Then you can make the shape of a plant you see on the trail.

Later you may make a painting from your sketch. If you have paints in a tray, you may take these on the trail.

Get a nickel and hike until you get to a spot where two trails cross. Flip the nickel.

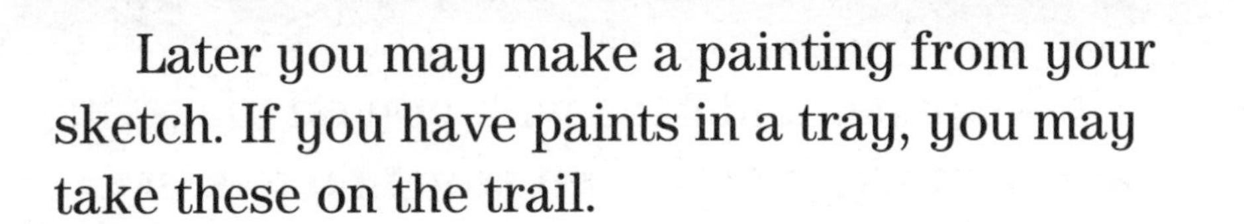

If the nickel lands on heads, then take a right. If it lands on tails, take a left.

Art Hike

Take paper and pens with you on the trail. Make a quick sketch when stopping to rest.

SRAonline.com

Printed in the United States of America.

Send all inquiries to this address:
SRA/McGraw-Hill
4400 Easton Commons
Columbus, OH 43219

The McGraw-Hill Companies

Meet the Bats

by Grace Trubiano
illustrated by Rachel Ivanyi

Decodable Story 20

Columbus, OH

Is that a flutter over the dark street? Is it a bird? Is it a bug? It may be a bat!

Bats keep the number of bugs down. So, we need bats. The next time you see bats, say thanks and wave!

How can bats help us?

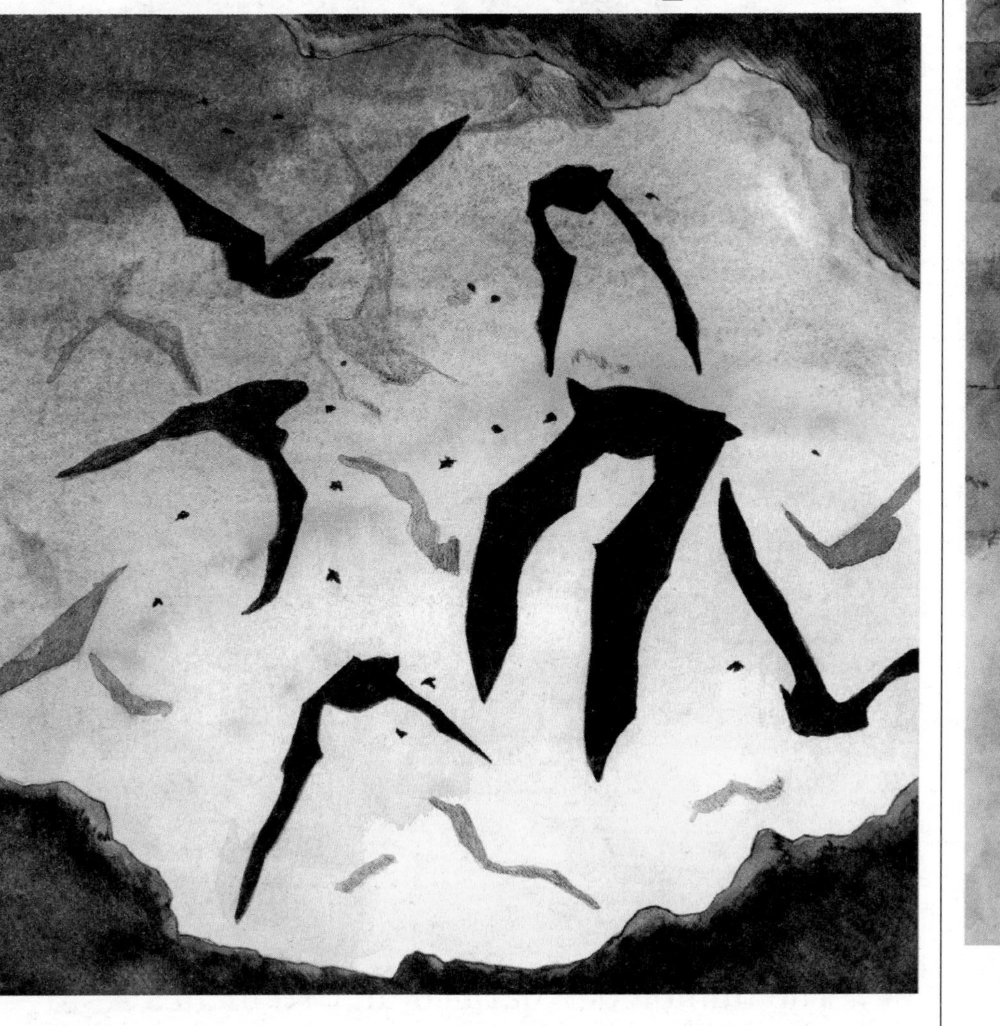

Did you know that bats like to eat bugs? They eat lots of bugs, even ones that bite us.

Bats are interesting animals. Do you know much about them? Read on to gather details about bats.

Are bats a kind of bird?

Both bats and birds have wings. So, bats and birds are alike in that way.

The bumblebee bat is only two inches from wing to wing! A big bat may reach five feet from wing to wing.

How big are bats?

Each kind of bat is a different size. Some bats are big, and some bats are little.

But bats are mammals, not birds. Birds have feathers. Mammals do not. A bat is the only mammal that can flap its wings and travel in the air.

Can bats see into the dark?

All bats can see. But bats use a different way to "see" in the dark.

In the day, bats sleep. Bats may stay in caves or in trees. When they sleep, bats hang upside down!

Where do bats live?

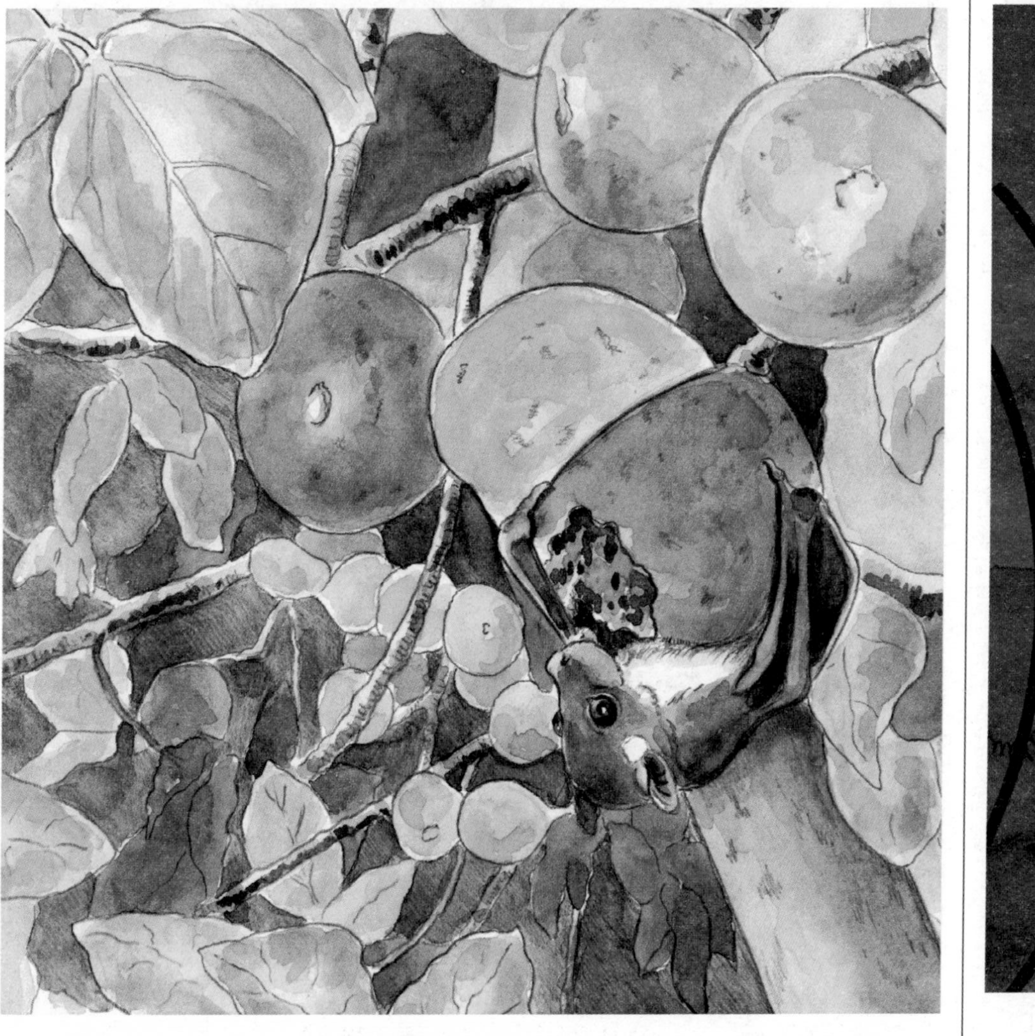

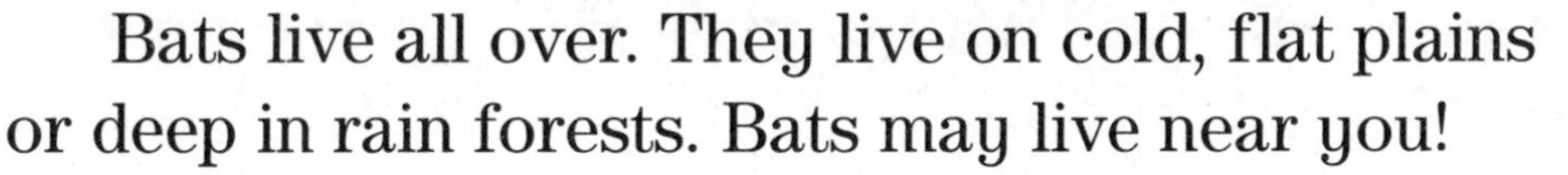

Bats live all over. They live on cold, flat plains or deep in rain forests. Bats may live near you!

Bats make calls and then wait. The call travels away from the bat and may hit an object.

Then the call returns to the bat. The bat's brain can tell from where the call is returning.

The bat realizes that an object is near. That way, the bat will not bump into things. Or, it may find bugs to eat!

SRAonline.com

Printed in the United States of America.

Send all inquiries to this address:
SRA/McGraw-Hill
4400 Easton Commons
Columbus, OH 43219

The McGraw-Hill Companies

Granddaddy Spider and the Party

an African tale retold by Gordon Thomas
illustrated by Rachel Ivanyi

Decodable Story 21

Columbus, OH

Now, spiders have little waists. But that was not always the way. Here is the story of how that happened.

By then, Granddaddy Spider's waist was tiny. And it remains that way to this day!

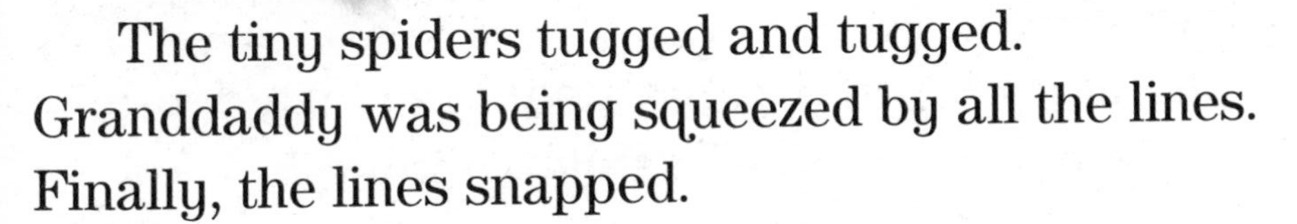

The tiny spiders tugged and tugged. Granddaddy was being squeezed by all the lines. Finally, the lines snapped.

One sunny day, Granddaddy Spider studied the bees as they gathered golden, sticky dust from a daisy.

"What will you do with all that dust?" asked nosey Granddaddy.

"Carry it back to the hive," buzzed the bees. "We need lots for the party."

Chimpanzee's and Zebra's parties started, too. Here came a third tug and then another.

In three days, Donkey's party started. A tiny spider tugged on the line. Just then Elephant's party started, and there was another tug.

"A party? That's funny," said Granddaddy. "I didn't hear of any party."

Granddaddy Spider went home. He drummed on his web to contact his grandkids. They were in each corner of the jungle. “Come home quickly!” he asked.

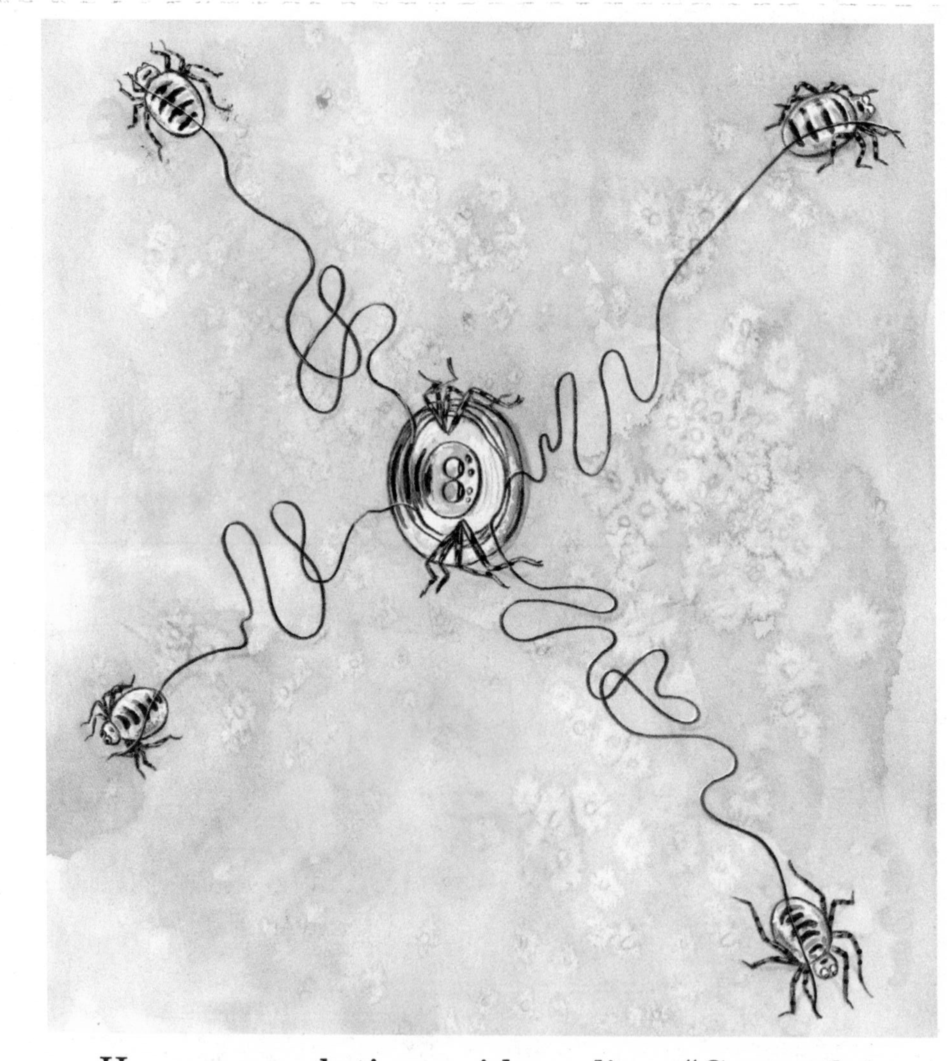

He gave each tiny spider a line. “Carry these with you to your corner. When a party starts, tug on the line. Then I will know where to go.”

Granddaddy needed to know when a party started. He made a plan. He spun four long, silky lines. He wrapped each line around his middle.

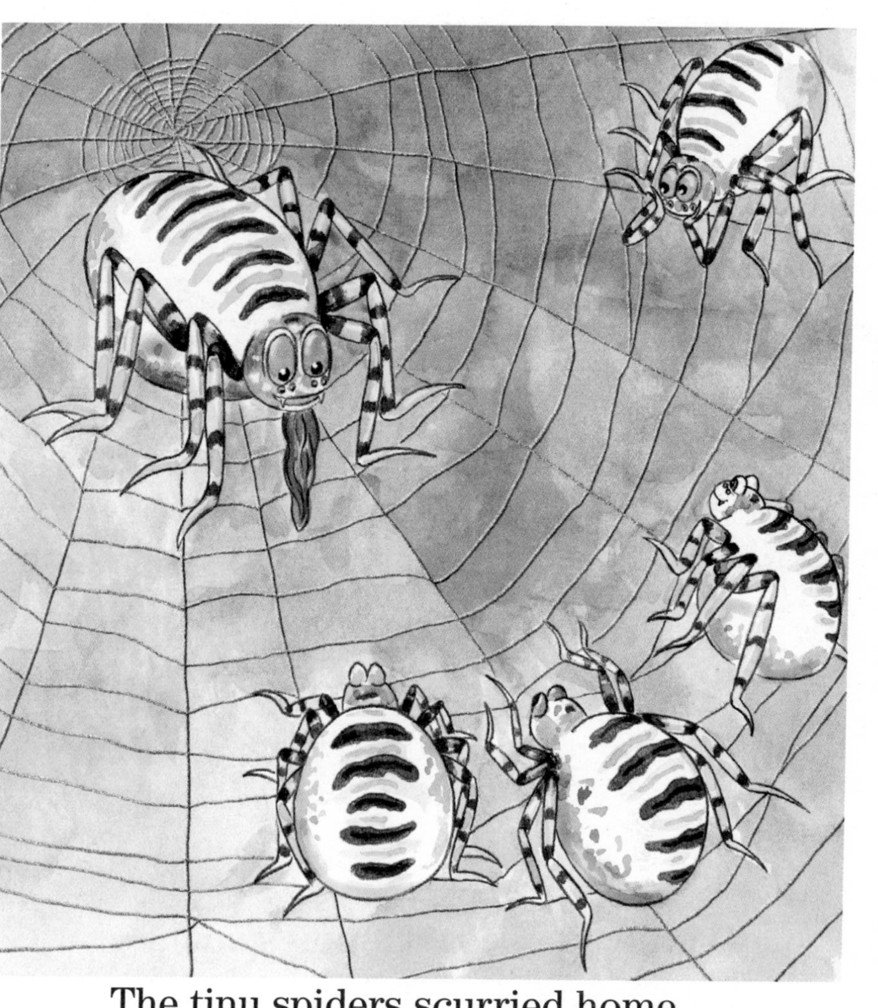

The tiny spiders scurried home. “What is it, Granddaddy?” they asked.

“Who is going to have a party?” Granddaddy asked.

"It is Donkey," said a tiny spider.

"It is Elephant," said another.

"It is Chimpanzee," said a third.

"It is Zebra," said the last.

"I cannot believe it!" Granddaddy said. "Four parties? And each is in a different corner of the jungle? How funny! But when?"

No one had any idea.

SRAonline.com

SRA

Printed in the United States of America.

Send all inquiries to this address:
SRA/McGraw-Hill
4400 Easton Commons
Columbus, OH 43219

The McGraw-Hill Companies

SRA Decodable Stories

A Force in the Dirt

by Anna Marie Randolph
illustrated by Brenda Johnson

Decodable Story 22

Columbus, OH

Greetings, readers! It's Ace Reporter here. This morning, we are down in the dirt! And we have a chance to chat with Grace.

Ace Reporter: Thank you, Grace. And thanks to your force, too. Let's face it. We need you in the dirt!

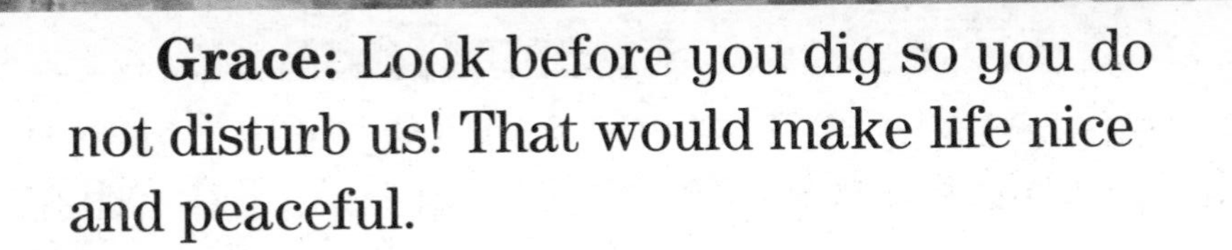

Grace: Look before you dig so you do not disturb us! That would make life nice and peaceful.

Grace is an officer of the dirt. She is at the center of the important jobs here.

Ace Reporter: Please tell us, Grace. What important jobs do you and your force perform each day?

68

Ace Reporter: Grace, before I head back up, do you have advice for those on top of the dirt?

77

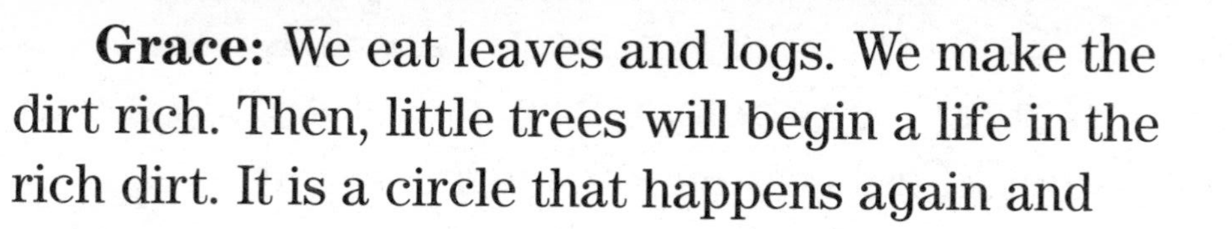

Grace: We eat leaves and logs. We make the dirt rich. Then, little trees will begin a life in the rich dirt. It is a circle that happens again and again.

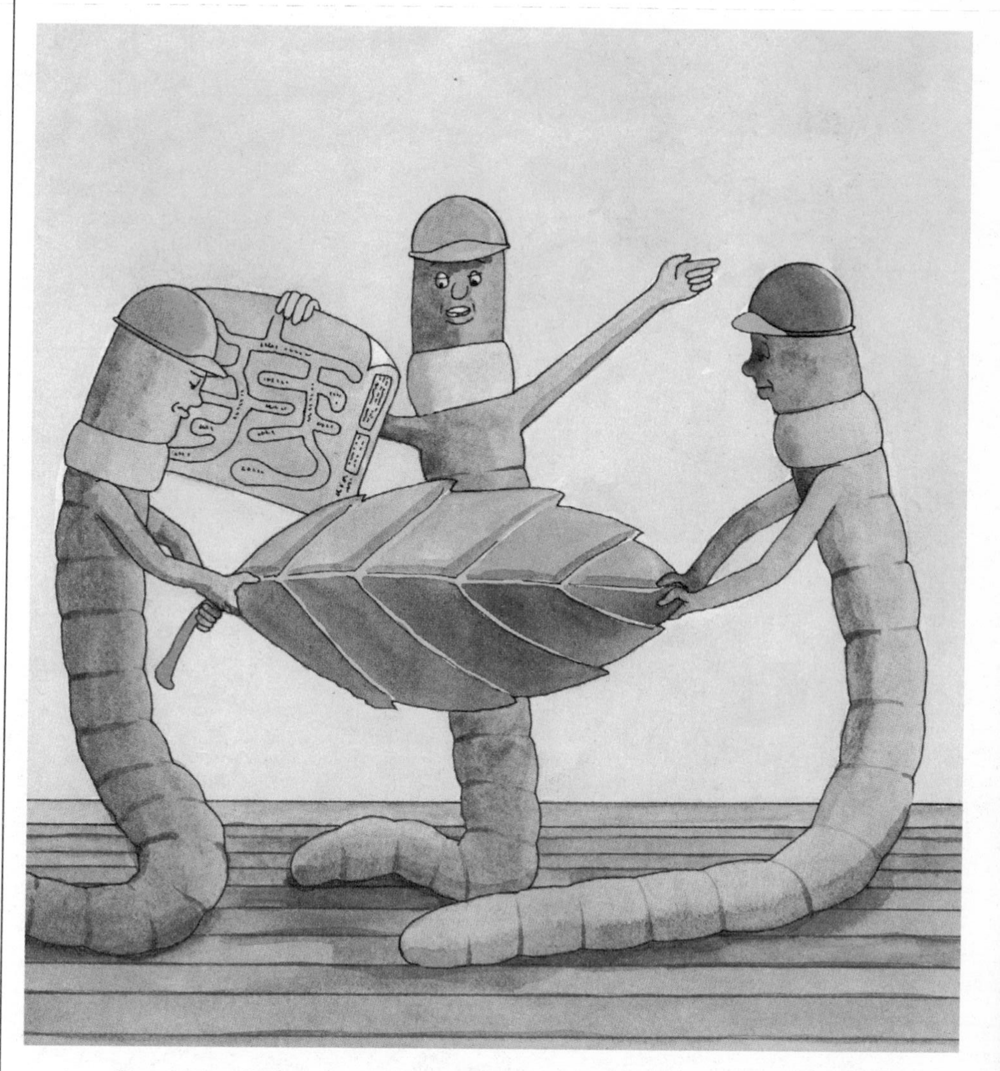

Grace: We do so much down here! You may not notice us down in the dirt, but we perform important jobs each day.

Grace: Remember all the leaves and plants that fell? If we did not do our job, all those leaves would stay where they fell.

Grace: No problem, Ace. It is not a big place. It is not like the home of a prince or princess.

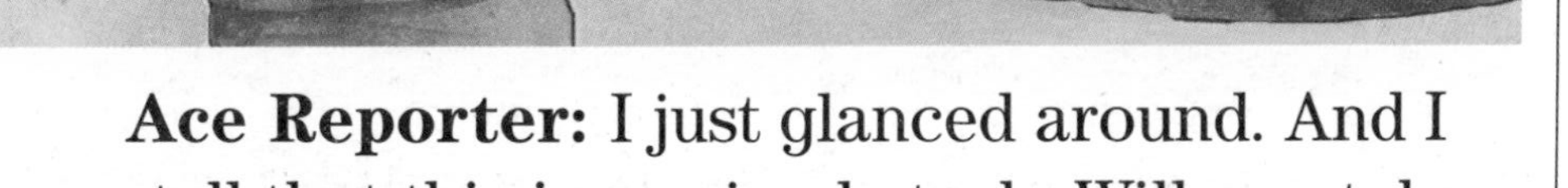

Ace Reporter: I just glanced around. And I can tell that this is no simple task. Will you take us around the place?

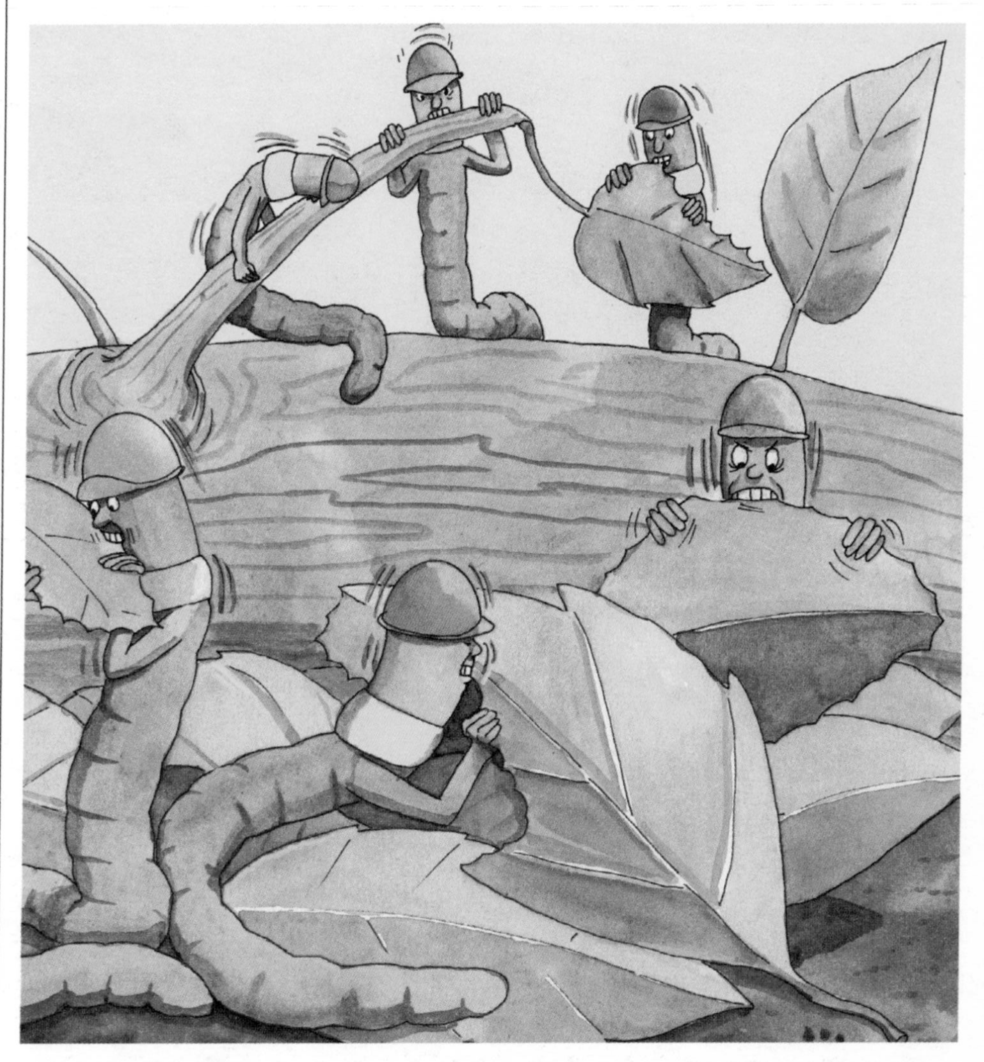

Our job is to eat that dead stuff up. We mince it up and turn it into rich dirt.

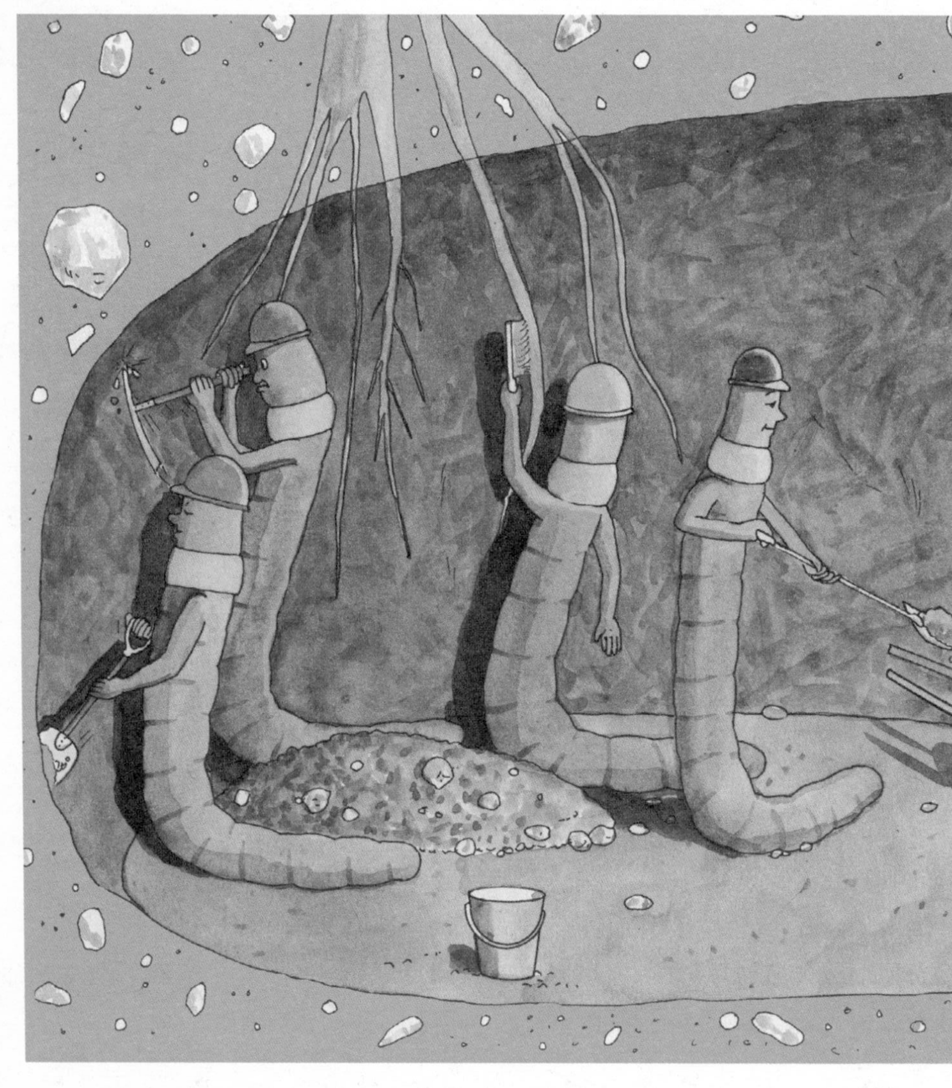

Grace: We make tunnels in the dirt, too. These little spaces help plants live well.

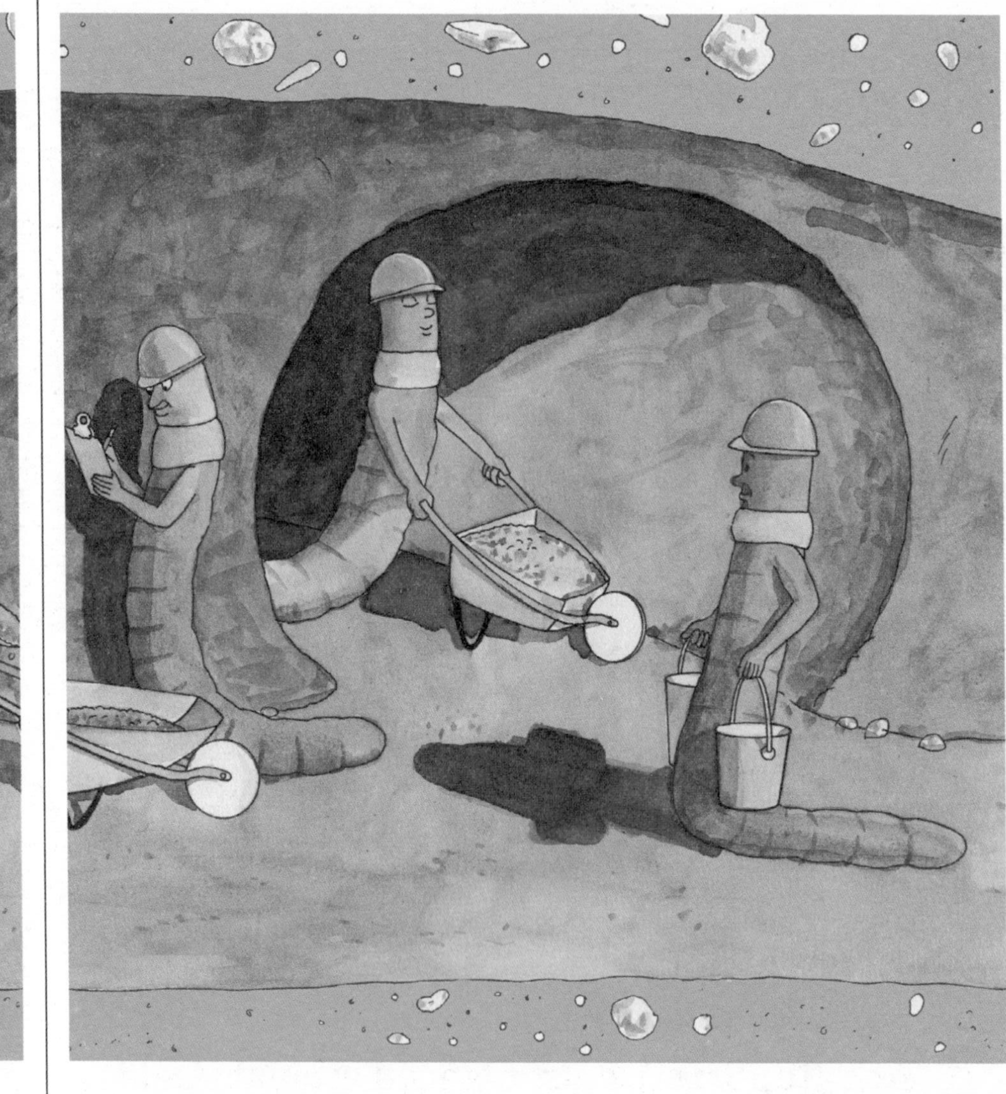

This does not cost a single cent! And let me tell you, Ace. This is a hard job. It is not a cinch.

SRAonline.com

Printed in the United States of America.

Send all inquiries to this address:
SRA/McGraw-Hill
4400 Easton Commons
Columbus, OH 43219

The McGraw-Hill Companies

Uncle Gene

by Gordon Thomas
illustrated by Stephanie Pershing

Decodable Story 23

Columbus, OH

"Hello, Roger!" said Uncle Gene. "I have an urgent matter to share with you, if I could just remember it!"

"Uncle Gene!" said Roger.

"With a giant tomato," said Roger.

"Wait!" said Uncle Gene. "That does not make sense! And it's what I was going to say!"

"Did I say *from* space?" said Uncle Gene. "I mean that it has an open space and a gem inside."

"We can have it for lunch," said Uncle Gene.

"What was it?" Uncle Gene asked. "A gingerbread man ran away! You may need to help catch him."

"Uncle Gene!" said Roger.

"Maybe not," Uncle Gene said. "There is a giant tomato bulging from the birdcage!"

"Uncle Gene!" said Roger.

"It's a kind of rock," said Uncle Gene. "It's from space."

"Uncle Gene!" said Roger.

"It's great!" said Roger. "What kind of rock is this?"

"It is a geode," said Uncle Gene.

"What is a geode?" asked Roger.

"Well, I'm thinking," said Uncle Gene. "What could that urgent matter be? I remember! I am supposed to give you this present."

Roger smiled and grabbed the present. "Great! Thank you," he said.

So Uncle Gene gave the rock a gentle tap. It broke apart. Roger got it out of the sock.

Uncle Gene said, "I will hit the rock with the hammer. I will be gentle."

"But that will hurt the rock!" said Roger.

Uncle Gene had a huge grin.

"Open it up!" said Uncle Gene. "There are no germs on it."

Roger opened the present. Inside was a rock.

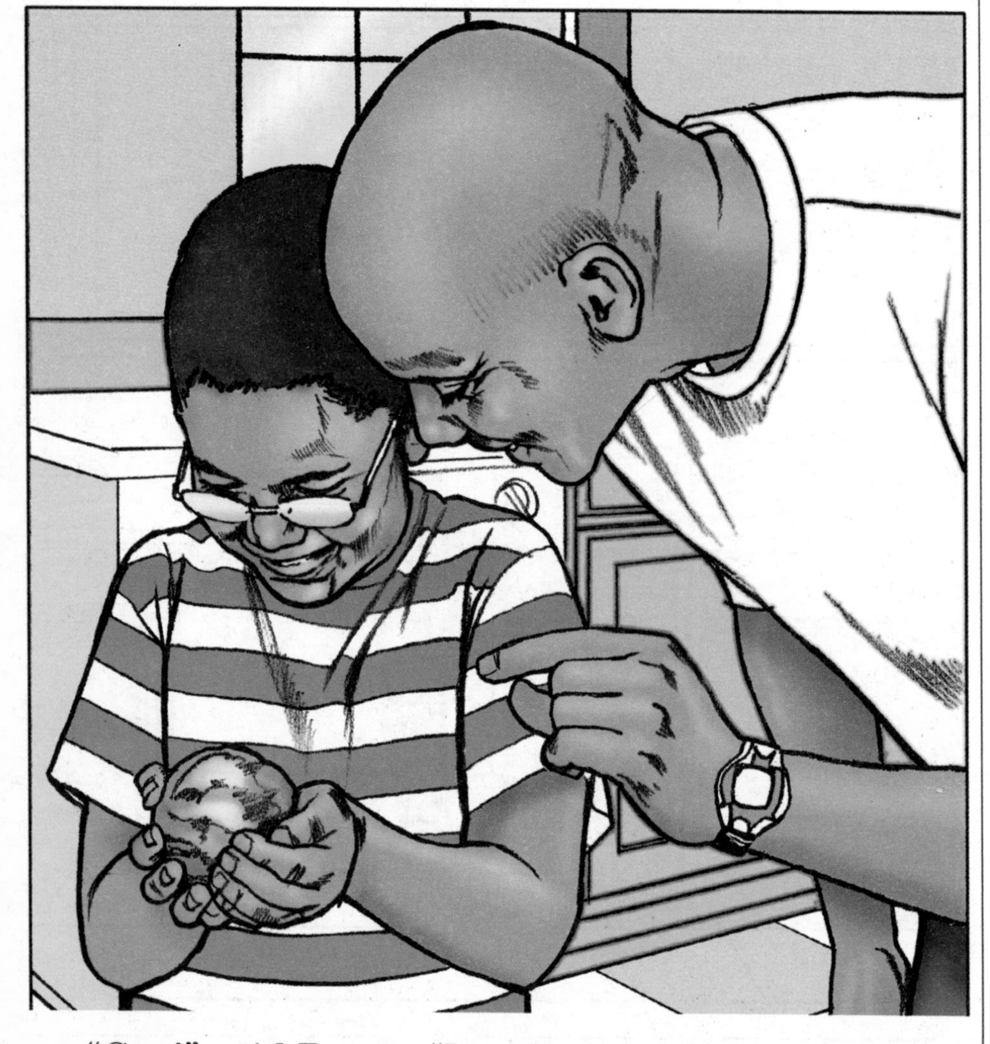

"Gee!" said Roger. "It is shaped like the Earth."

"It is not quite as large," said Uncle Gene. "I need a sock and a hammer."

Roger did not understand this. "Place the rock inside the sock," said Uncle Gene. "That will keep you from danger."

SRAonline.com

Printed in the United States of America.

Send all inquiries to this address:
SRA/McGraw-Hill
4400 Easton Commons
Columbus, OH 43219

The McGraw-Hill Companies

A Green Leaf Print

by Martin Smith
illustrated by Dave Fischer

Decodable Story 24

Columbus, OH

What is the main difference between plants and animals? Think about this. Can an animal's body make its own meal?

What other things can you do with a leaf print? That is a challenge for you!

Or you may make a spiral pad look fancy. Paste the print on the top. On the pages, sketch and write about trees! Write notes in the margins.

Well, green plants can feed themselves. Each plant is a little factory. Plants use the sun's rays to make a sweet substance. With that, plants can feed themselves.

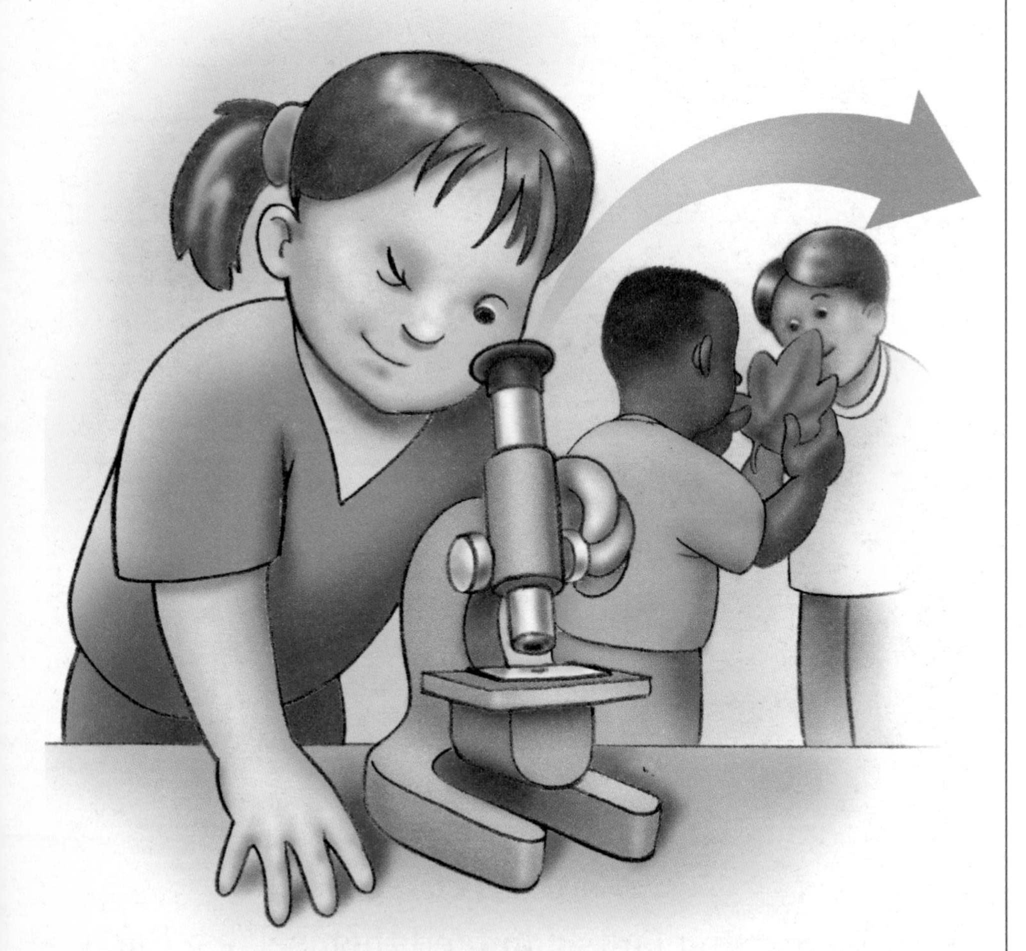

You can see a thin slice of a green leaf under a microscope. That would reveal cells, or tiny parts, of the leaf.

Now what will you do with a leaf print? You may make the print into a nice hanging. Simply paste the print to a stick and add twine.

When you are done beating the leaf, lift up the fabric. The leaf will have left its likeness in green.

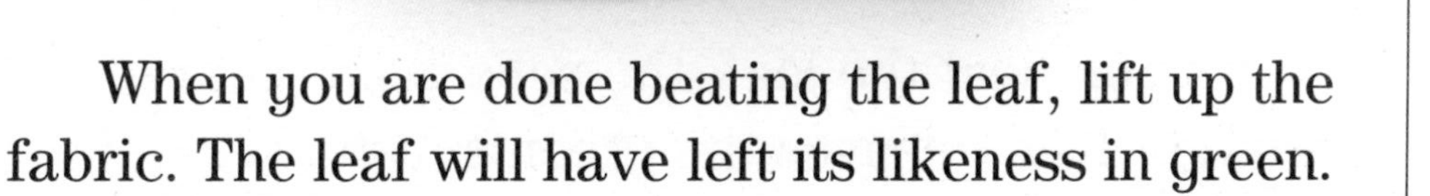

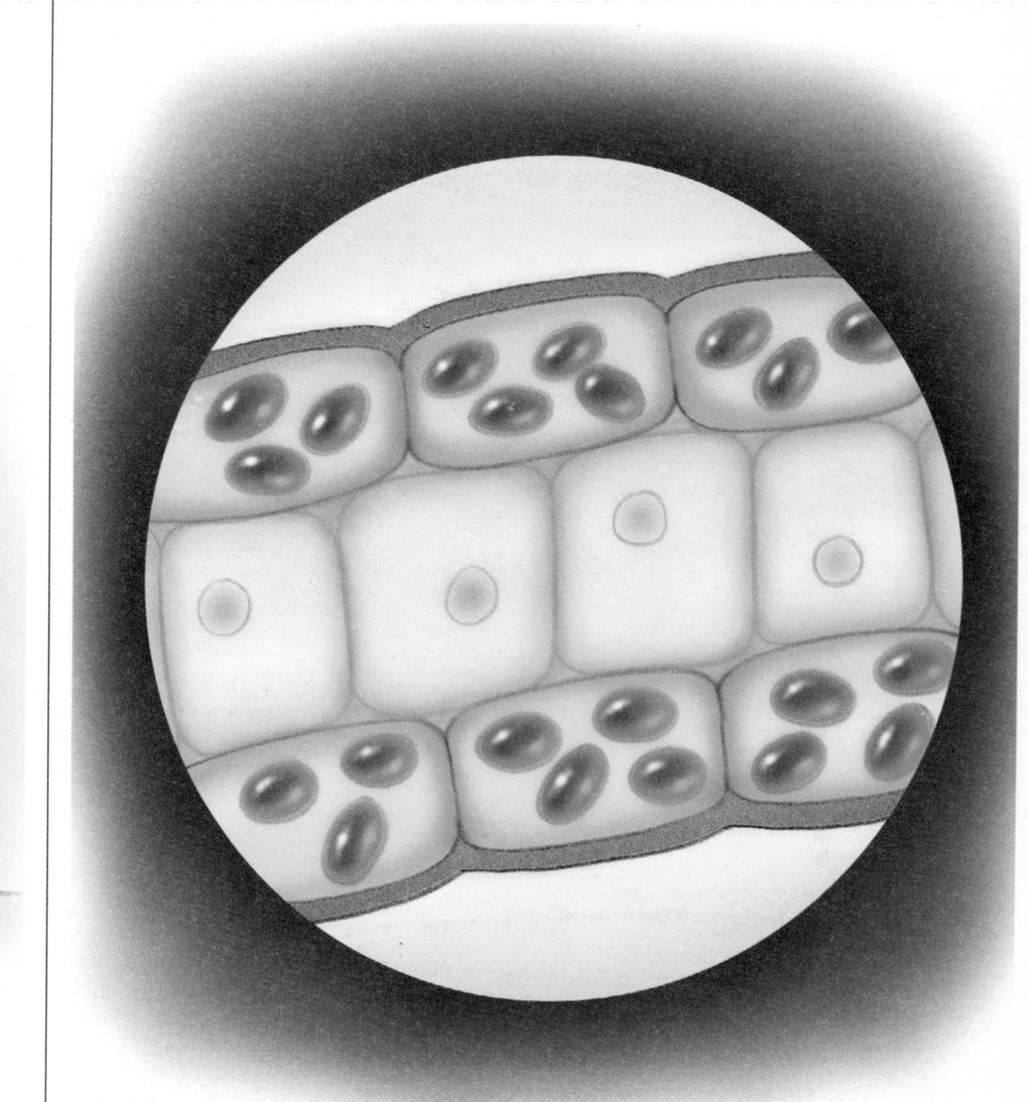

Several cells look like green jellybeans! These cells are the ones that get the job done.

Would you like to make a green leaf print? It is fun and easy to do.

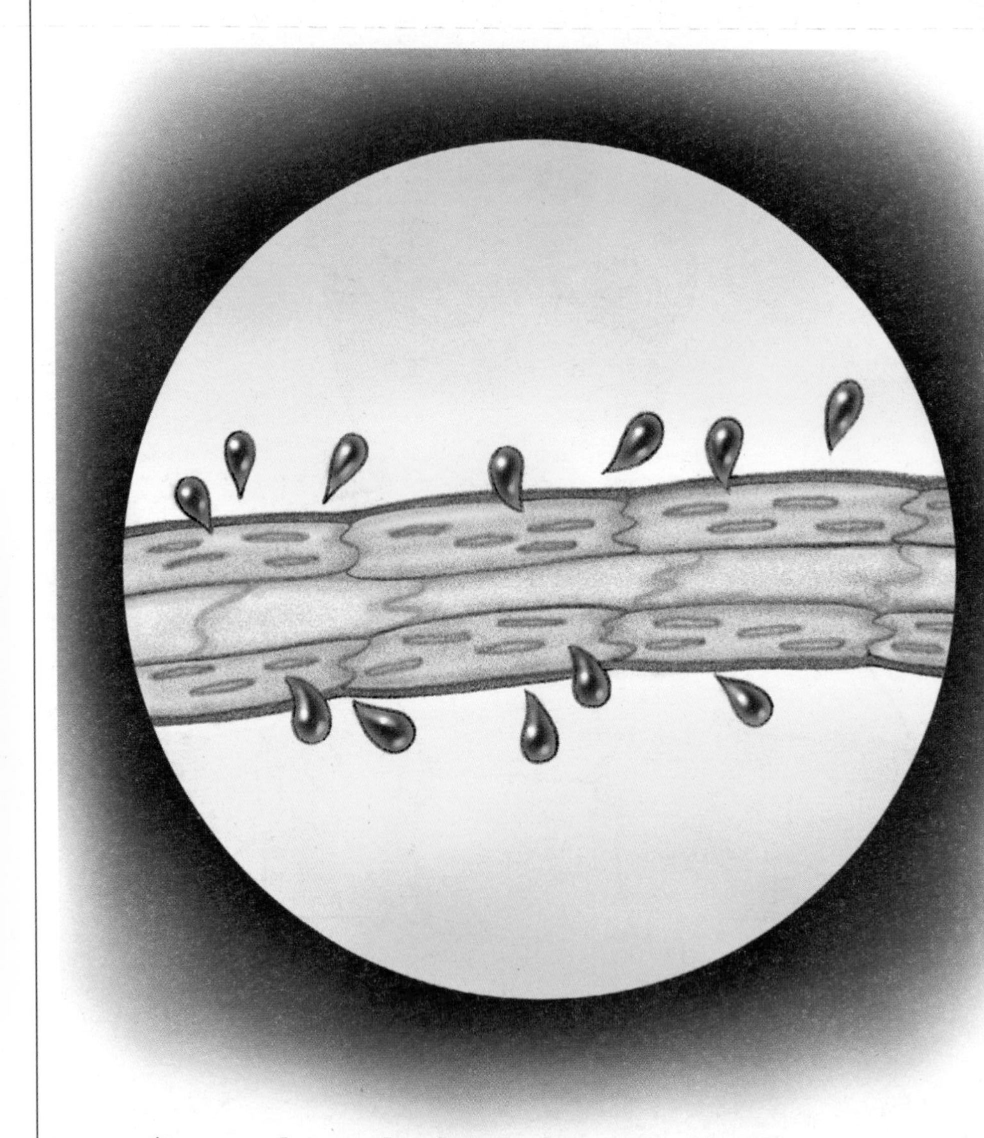

As you beat the leaf, the cells inside it are broken. This releases the green substance.

Use a rock to gently beat the fabric. Use even force. Trace around the edge of the leaf. Then beat the center.

Objects Needed to Make a Green Leaf Print

- green leaf
- piece of cotton fabric
- block
- thumbtacks
- rock

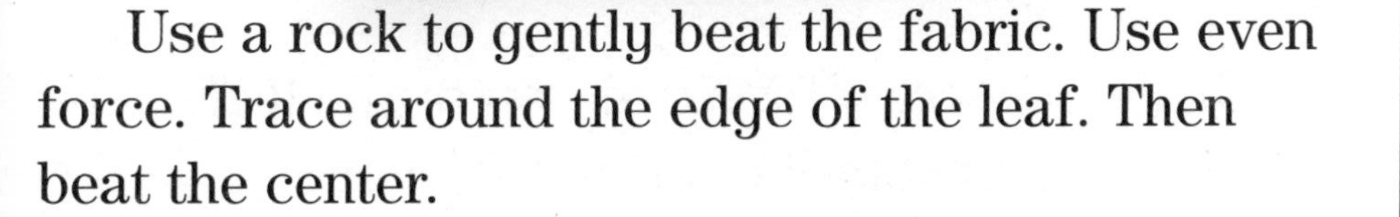

How to Make a Green Leaf Print

Start by picking a leaf from a tree. Wide, flat leaves will be best. Then lay the leaf on a block.

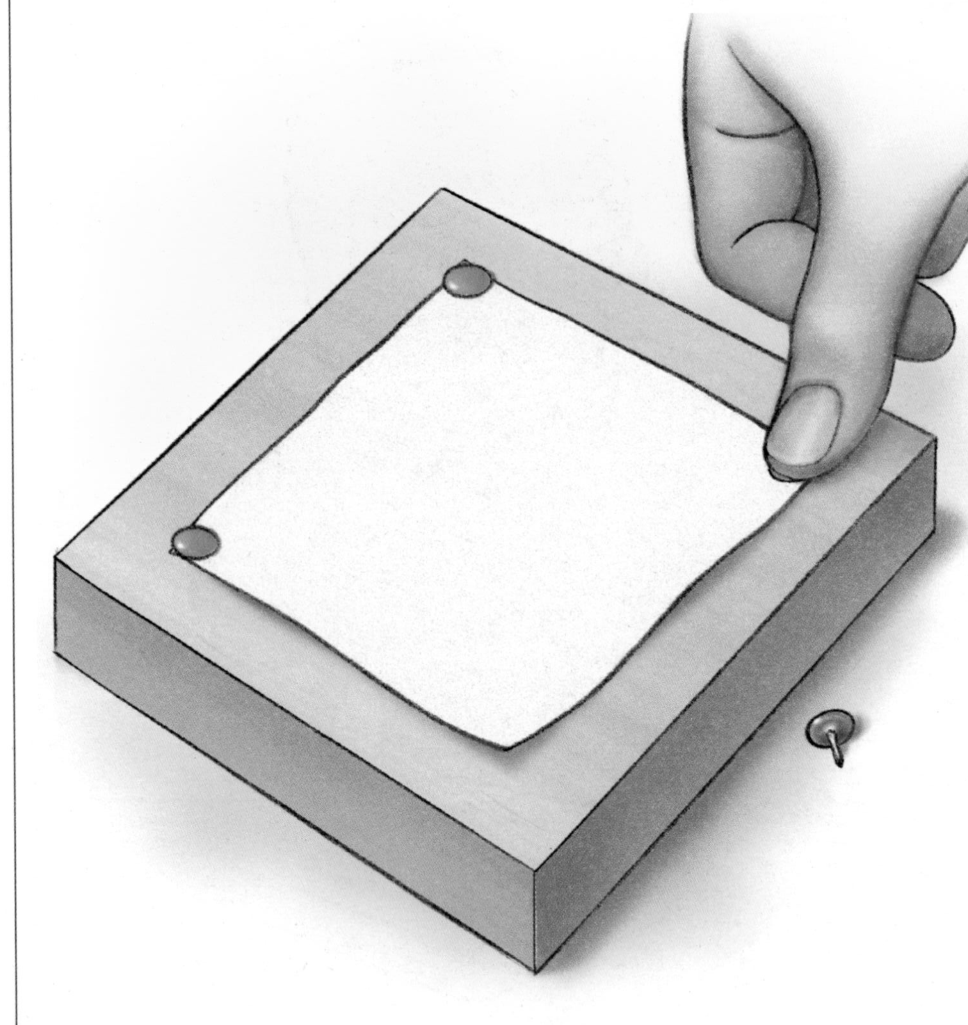

Place a piece of fabric on top of the leaf. Use thumbtacks to hold the fabric in place.

SRAonline.com

Printed in the United States of America.

Send all inquiries to this address:
SRA/McGraw-Hill
4400 Easton Commons
Columbus, OH 43219

The McGraw-Hill Companies

Meet the Firefighters

by Lynn Frankel
illustrated by Mary Kurnick Maass

Decodable Story 25

Columbus, OH

Hi! I'm Mike. Do you know what my job is? That's right! I'm a firefighter. I fight fires.

Well, time to head back. It was a delight to meet you! And remember, check your fire alarms! It just might save a life!

That's what you need to do, too. If you are ever in a fire, stay down and get out fast. Do not hide! It's wise to keep a flashlight near the bed.

This is where I work. It's open all the time. Fires can happen at any time. So, we firefighters work day and night.

This is our fire truck. Like most fire trucks, it's red and white. We scrub and wax it a lot. We like it clean and bright.

There are times we must go in. Smoke rises, so we stay down. Smoke is dark. We use our lights. We get out as fast as we can.

There are times we need to get up high to fight a fire. Then we use ladders. This ladder can reach higher than 100 feet!

If there is a fire, this alarm bell rings. There are times when I'm asleep, and the bell rings. What a fright!

All the lights go on, and all the firefighters run. Some run down the flight of steps. I like to slide down the pole.

Some firefighters get the hose ready. Then they turn on the water. It comes out quite strongly.

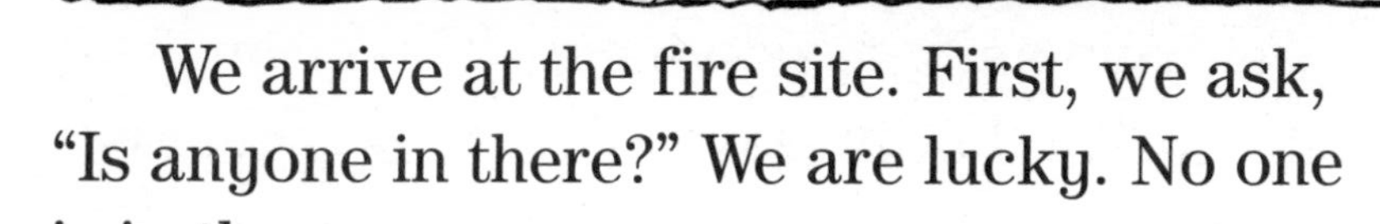

We arrive at the fire site. First, we ask, "Is anyone in there?" We are lucky. No one is in there.

We get into the fire truck. Five firefighters ride this night. Let me tell you, it's pretty tight in there!

This fire truck needs two drivers. One drives in the regular spot, and one drives in the back.

We drive as fast as we can. The siren screams. The lights flash. This tells drivers, "Get out of our way!"

SRAonline.com

SRA

Printed in the United States of America.

Send all inquiries to this address:
SRA/McGraw-Hill
4400 Easton Commons
Columbus, OH 43219

The McGraw·Hill Companies

Try My Pie

by Luke Fisher
illustrated by Mark Corcoran

Decodable Story 26

SRA

Columbus, OH

Tyler came into the bakery. It smells so good! He licked his lips. Mrs. Bly bakes treats for him to try.

"I can't lie," Tyler cried. "This is a great pie! In fact, I'm going to eat this little pie all by myself!"

"I'd like to see you try," said Mrs. Bly.

"Now, Tyler," Mrs. Bly smiled. "Aren't you glad you tried my chicken pot pie?"

Tyler spied Mrs. Bly by the stove. "Hi, Tyler!" she yelled. "You're just in time! This little pie is piping hot. It's just waiting for you to try."

"No, thanks, Mrs. Bly," Tyler said, looking away.

"Now, don't be shy," she said. "Just give the pie a try."

"Okay, I give up!" Tyler yelled. "I'll try your chicken pot pie!" He had a tiny bite. Then he had a bigger bite, and then a bigger one.

“Now, it’s time to try my chicken pot pie. I’m telling you, this pie is yummy! It’s so yummy, you’ll want to cry!”

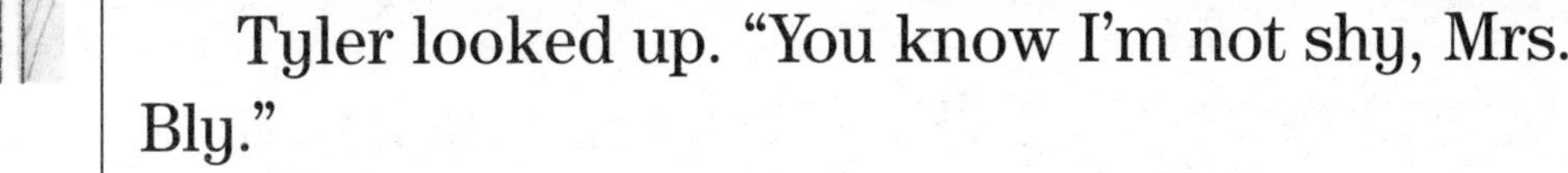

Tyler looked up. “You know I’m not shy, Mrs. Bly.”

“Then why will you not try my pie?” she asked.

“I can’t deny it,” Tyler sighed. “I just don’t like pie, Mrs. Bly.”

"YOU DON'T LIKE PIE?" Mrs. Bly yelled to the bakers in the back. "Did you hear that? He said he does not like pie!"

"You need to make all those flies fly away from the pie."

"Fly away, flies. Fly away."

Mrs. Bly smiled. “Yes, chicken and veggies are in this pie. This pie is not sweet, but even flies want a try!”

She turned back to Tyler. “How can you not like pie? Why, that’s like saying you don’t like the sky! Or that birds can’t fly! Or that spies don’t pry!”

Mrs. Bly put the pie under Tyler's nose.

"You just have not tried the right pie. I baked this pie all by myself. It's my best chicken pot pie."

"Chicken pot pie?" Tyler asked. "Do you mean there is chicken in that pie?"

SRAonline.com

SRA

Printed in the United States of America.

Send all inquiries to this address:
SRA/McGraw-Hill
4400 Easton Commons
Columbus, OH 43219

The McGraw-Hill Companies

The Boat Show

by Luke Fisher
illustrated by Jan Pyk

Decodable Story 27

SRA

Columbus, OH

Hope's home is Oak Cove, a little city along the coast. Every October, Oak Cove hosts its own boat show. This October, Hope is going to be in the show!

"What kind of boat do you want to own?" Mrs. Dole asked. "A sailboat, a rowboat, or a motorboat?"

Hope chuckled. "I just want a boat that floats!"

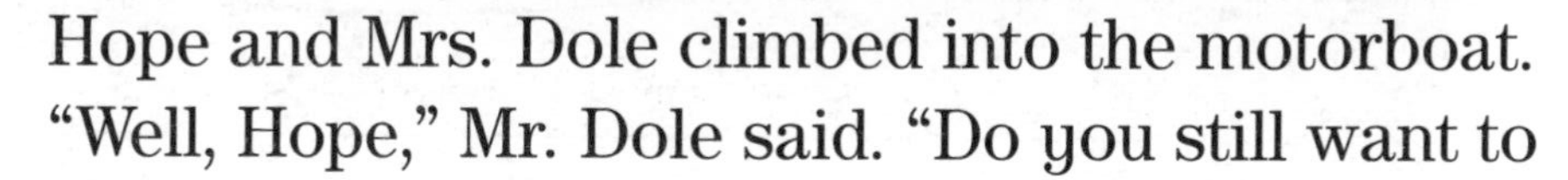

Hope and Mrs. Dole climbed into the motorboat.

"Well, Hope," Mr. Dole said. "Do you still want to sail your own boat in the show when you're grown up?"

"I do!" she replied.

Hope chatted with all her pals.

"I'm sailing with Mr. and Mrs. Dole in the boat show!" she boasted. "They told me I can sail my own boat when I'm grown up."

The day of the boat show finally arrived. Hope met Mr. Dole at the docks.

"Hi, Hope!" he called.

They both were ready to swim to shore. Then, they saw a boat approaching. It was Mr. Dole!

Hope and Mrs. Dole tried to lighten the load. They started to throw heavy things overboard. But the boat kept sinking lower and lower.

"Hi, Mr. Dole! It's a great day for a boat show!"

"I don't know, Hope," Mr. Dole looked up at the flagpole.

The flag was not waving.

"No!" moaned Hope. "We can't sail without wind!"

Mrs. Dole rowed and rowed. But the boat didn't go.

"No!" Hope groaned. "Water is flowing into the boat!"

"There must be a hole!" Mrs. Dole yelled.

Hope and Mrs. Dole hopped into the rowboat.
"I'll follow you in the motorboat," Mr. Dole said.
Hope rowed first. Then it was Mrs. Dole's turn.

Hope sat on the dock and moped.
"I told everyone I know to come see me in the show!"

Mrs. Dole patted Hope on the back.

"Don't mope, Hope," Mrs. Dole said. "We can't sail. But we can still be in the boat show."

"Do you want to use our rowboat or our motorboat?" she asked.

"The rowboat!" Hope jumped up. "It'll be fun to row!"

SRAonline.com

SRA

Printed in the United States of America.

Send all inquiries to this address:
SRA/McGraw-Hill
4400 Easton Commons
Columbus, OH 43219

The McGraw-Hill Companies

Apples Up High

by Eileen Breeze
illustrated by Olivia Cole

Decodable Story 28

SRA

Columbus, OH

Our class is taking a trip to an apple orchard. Before we go, Ms. Wright tells us how apples grow. She shows us photos of an orchard.

I pick an apple from the pile and clean it as fast as I can. Then, I take a big crunchy bite. Mmmm—what a yummy snack!

"Let's each pick an apple to try," suggests Ms. Wright. "But, we must clean them first," she adds.

The yellow bus pulls away and heads to the orchard. "It's a fine day for picking apples!" exclaims our bus driver, Mr. Clive.

"There are many kinds of apples to pick," shares Ms. Wright. "Cortland, Rome, and Granny Smith are some of them."

"I wish I could make cider!" cries Joan.
"I hope I can make a pie," adds Kyle.
Me? I just want to snack on a crunchy apple!

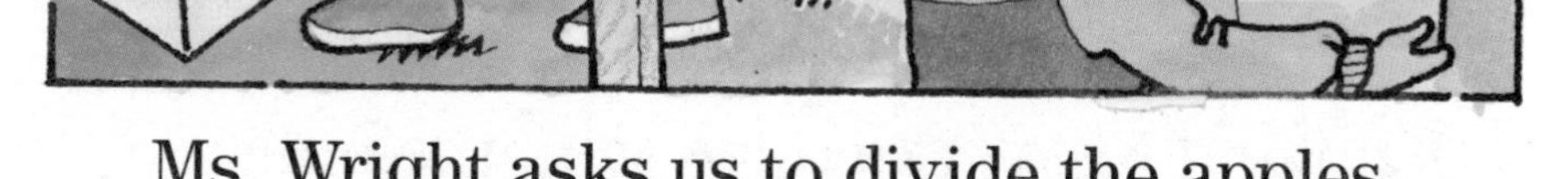

Ms. Wright asks us to divide the apples into three piles. We divide them into Cortland, Rome, and Granny Smith.

Farmer Grove tells us the right way to pick apples. Then, he gives us a box and a picking pole. Joan and I carry the box. Kyle grabs the picking pole.

In the orchard, we see row after row of trees. The trees grow high, right up to the sky!

Joan and Kyle take turns with the pole. Before long, our box has a load of apples that we carry back to the barn.

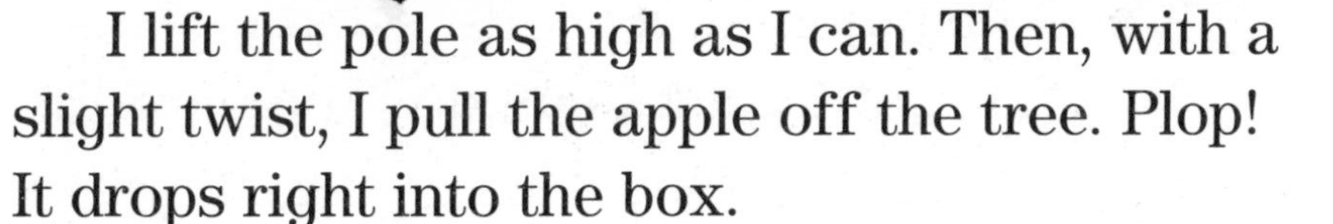

I lift the pole as high as I can. Then, with a slight twist, I pull the apple off the tree. Plop! It drops right into the box.

As we stroll between the rows, Ms. Wright shows us Cortland trees. “Can we pick from these?” I ask.

"Joan, will you hold the box? Kyle, may I try the picking pole?" I ask. I roll up my sleeves and grab the pole.

The pole is long, and not very light.

"Can I help you lift it?" offers Joan.

"Thanks, but I think I can do it by myself," I reply.

SRAonline.com

Printed in the United States of America.

Send all inquiries to this address:
SRA/McGraw-Hill
4400 Easton Commons
Columbus, OH 43219

The McGraw-Hill Companies

A Stroll on Mule Avenue

by Edward Bricker
illustrated by Mary Kurnick Maass

Decodable Story 29

Columbus, OH

Music from an alarm wakes me up. I see the sun. Is it time to get up?

"What a fun time we had, cutie!" exclaims Dad. "Yes, it was fun to walk on Mule Avenue!" I say. Dad and I hum tunes all the way home.

Our last stop is the Value-Shop. Dad helps me find a nice costume for my musical.

The huge clock on my dresser reads 7:35. But it's Saturday morning! A few more winks, and then I'll get up!

Dad is singing a tune as I walk in.

"Hi, cutie!" he sings, as he turns off the alarm. "Did my music wake you?"

"The Mule Avenue Bakery! Dad, can we go in?" We do just that and leave with a huge loaf of bread!

After, we walk across the avenue. Dad lets me use the key to open our mailbox. I see a few letters inside. One is for me!

"I made a huge stack of pancakes. Grab a few!"

"Thanks. Where are you going?" I ask.

"To Mule Avenue to run a few errands," he replies.

"Mule Avenue? Can I go, too?"

"Yes," replies Dad. "But first eat a few more pancakes. Mule Avenue is quite a walk. You'll need the fuel!"

A few moments later we arrive at the vet's. Dad needs to get some pills to cure Mac's cold.

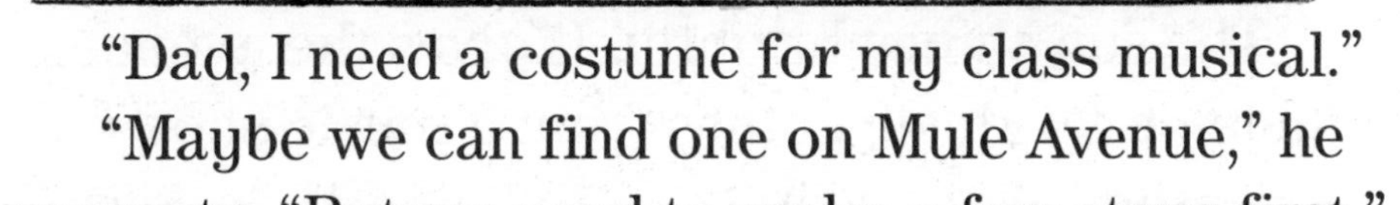

“Dad, I need a costume for my class musical.”

“Maybe we can find one on Mule Avenue,” he suggests. “But we need to make a few stops first.”

I finish eating a few pancakes. Then I run to get dressed. What will I put on for my walk on Mule Avenue? My shirt with the red cubes!

"Cute shirt!" exclaims Dad. "I like the fun cubes. Grab your coat, and let's get going. We have a lot to do on Mule Avenue."

The sun shines brightly. It gives the avenue a golden hue. Music comes from a music shop on the corner. What a fine day to be on Mule Avenue!

SRAonline.com

SRA

Printed in the United States of America.

Send all inquiries to this address:
SRA/McGraw-Hill
4400 Easton Commons
Columbus, OH 43219

The McGraw-Hill Companies

The Kitten's Rescue

by Edward Bricker
illustrated by Mary Kurnick Maass

Decodable Story 30

SRA

Columbus, OH

From my window I see Mrs. Fuse gazing up a tree. She is using a stick to poke the branches.

"Thank you for rescuing Hugo!" cries Mrs. Fuse.

"Don't thank us," replies the Fire Chief. "Thank this smart fellow for calling. He helped rescue Hugo. Sam was the real hero today!"

They use their tallest ladder to climb the tree. A few moments later, Hugo is rescued.

"Hugo!" cries Mrs. Fuse, "You gave us quite a fright today!"

"Are you okay, Mrs. Fuse?" I ask.

"No!" she cries. "My kitten, Hugo, is stuck in the tree!"

"Hugo likes to see from the tree. But the tree is high, and he is afraid. Do you have a ladder we can use to rescue Hugo?"

Hugo starts to mew and does not stop.
"I think he's scared!" cries Mrs. Fuse.
"We'll rescue Hugo as fast as we can," replies the Chief.

"We're here to rescue a cute little kitten," declares the Chief.

"That's Hugo. He's sitting on that huge branch at the top of the tree!" cries Mrs. Fuse.

"No, I don't," I tell Mrs. Fuse. "But I will call the Fire Chief. He will rescue Hugo."

"Thank you, Sam!" cries Mrs. Fuse.

"Mrs. Fuse's cat, Hugo, is stuck in a tree," I tell Mom. "I need to help rescue him."

When the red truck stops, a few firefighters jump off the back. The Fire Chief runs over to Mrs. Fuse and me.

A few moments later, we see a huge red fire truck. It is turning right onto Cuba Avenue.

"Use this," Mom suggests, as she hands me her cell phone.

I make the call, and a nice lady responds, "Fire and Rescue, can I help you?"

"Yes," I say. "A cute little kitten named Hugo is trapped in a tree. The tree is in my yard. Can you come to rescue him?"

"My name is Sam Smith. I live at 35 Cuba Avenue."

"I'll send the fire truck right away," she replies.

SRAonline.com

Printed in the United States of America.

Send all inquiries to this address:
SRA/McGraw-Hill
4400 Easton Commons
Columbus, OH 43219

The McGraw-Hill Companies

The Museum

by Eileen Breeze
illustrated by Mary Kurnick Maass

Decodable Story 31

Columbus, OH

Hubert liked to play with his helicopter.
"Want to play with me, Pamela?" he asked.
"No, it's way too hot in the sun," she said.
Pamela picked up another ice cube.

"Today I learned that museums *are* amusing," said Hubert. "Thanks for taking us to the museum, Dad!"

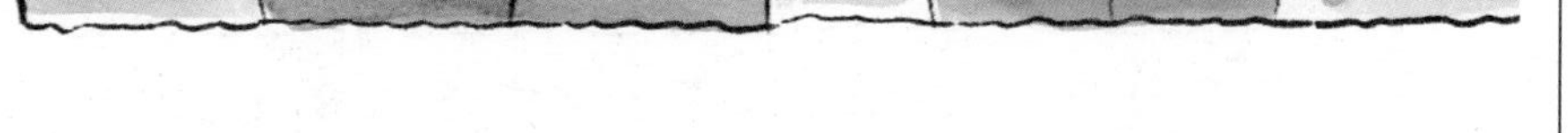

“So, what did you think of the museum?” asked Dad.

“Neat,” said Pamela. “I liked the music best!”

“Let’s go to a museum,” said Dad.

“Not a museum!” cried Hubert. “I don’t want to go. Museums are boring!”

“A few museums are amusing,” argued Pamela.

“Museums can have lots of fun things,” added Dad.

“Like what?” mumbled Hubert.

“Like helicopters, planes…”

In a few seconds, the lights dimmed.

“It’s dark in here,” whispered Hubert.

Then bright white stars started to shine. Before long, they lit up the entire sky.

“This place is packed!” said Pamela. “There are just a few empty seats.”

“I see three over there,” said Hubert.

Then they sat and waited for the show.

“Planes? Really? Can we go, Dad?” asked Hubert.

“But museums are *boring*, right?” teased Dad as he winked at Pamela.

“Well, maybe I’ll change my mind,” said Hubert.

Dad, Pamela, and Hubert drove eight miles to the museum.

"It's so huge!" cried Pamela.

"Yes, but it better have *amusing* things!" cried Hubert.

"That old one over there is huge!" cried Hubert.

"Think of all the fuel it used!" added Pamela.

“Eight planes! And they’re all flying!” gasped Hubert.

“They’re not really flying,” said Dad. “They’re hanging from wires.”

“What luck! Today the museum has a display on things that fly.”

“I *will* see planes!” cried Hubert.

“Is that music I hear?” asked Pamela.

“Yes,” Dad nodded. “It’s the music of birds! Let’s start there.”

"Look at these birds!" said Pamela. "Some are huge!"

"And some are sort of puny!" said Hubert.

"I like the cute yellow birds," said Pamela.

"Me, too," said Hubert. "But I like this red one best."

All the birds were flying and singing.

"That red bird is singing hip-hop music!" joked Dad.

"You're the *real* amusement here, Dad," cried Pamela.

SRAonline.com

Printed in the United States of America.

Send all inquiries to this address:
SRA/McGraw-Hill
4400 Easton Commons
Columbus, OH 43219

The McGraw-Hill Companies

Under the Moon

by Sean Saunders
illustrated by Brenda Johnson

Decodable Story 32

Columbus, OH

At noon the light is strong and you can see the animals. They shoo flies on the farm and play at the zoo.

Soon the sun will rise. The moon will set, and it will be light again. And only the animals know what happened last night.

What did you hear by the light of the moon? You have snooped with your ears, but have not seen the proof!

But soon it will be night. Darkness hides the animals. Then, only your ears can tell you who is out with the moon.

What is the first thing you hear? Is it a cricket's loud chirp in the grass? Or is it a bat's whoosh in the wind? Maybe it's a swallow's swoop to get food?

And what is that rushing whoosh in the leaves? The panther and the tiger are running in a loop. Who can zoom faster and win the race?

What's that chattering up on the roof? Is it a bunch of chipmunks in a goofy mood? Or is it a flock of birds creating a clatter?

Who else is there? If you hear a soft coo, a pigeon is there. Many little coos mean she has a brood, too.

Do you hear a hoot, hoot? A wise old bird perches high in the tree. Cluck, cluck, cluck means chickens in the coop.

When an animal roars back, it must be the lion in the zoo. And only the elephant has a nose that can toot to the moon.

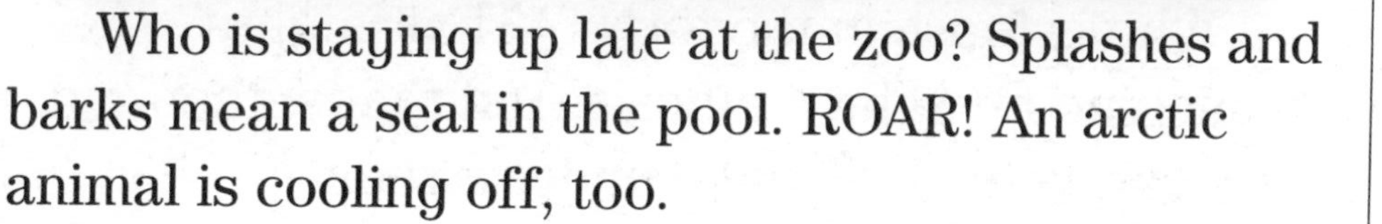

Who is staying up late at the zoo? Splashes and barks mean a seal in the pool. ROAR! An arctic animal is cooling off, too.

Who is in the field? Some say moo. And some do not say a thing—they are taking a snooze.

Who paddles on the lake, alongside the moon? A moan or a wail is the cry of a loon. Do you hear a honk? There is a goose afloat, too.

Who is loose in the forest? That mighty munching must be a moose! And that slither and hiss can only be a snake under a root.

SRAonline.com

Printed in the United States of America.

Send all inquiries to this address:
SRA/McGraw-Hill
4400 Easton Commons
Columbus, OH 43219

The McGraw-Hill Companies

A Robin's Red Plumes

retold by Elizabeth Ramsey
illustrated by Austin Fetter

Decodable Story 33

Columbus, OH

Some time ago, Rudy the Robin had plain feathers. It was Luna the Fox who gave the robin bright red plumes. Many people do not know the story. Here is how it happened.

To this day, all robins have a red chest. Animals and people admire the robin's red feathers. All tell the tale of how Rudy the Robin was brave and kind, and how Luna gave him bright red plumes.

Luna picked a tulip and dipped it in the water. She used it to paint Rudy's chest feathers red.

"These red plumes will stand out," she said. "I will know not to harm you."

It was June, and the animals were playful. Bruce the Raccoon was most playful of all.

Bruce was rude and liked to tease Luna. Bruce liked to trick Luna, too.

"Jump on my back!" Luna told Rudy. Luna ran to a secret place where the water ran red.

Luna was truly grateful.

"Kind Rudy, you helped me. Now it is my duty to help you!" Luna said.

Luna was playing a tune on her flute. Bruce challenged Luna to a race. Truth be told, Luna could run faster. But Bruce started first.

The race was a ruse to get Luna to the river. Bruce ran up a dune on the river's bank. He peered into the water.

"Luna, I am just a plain bird," Rudy began. "I will help you if you will not hurt me."

Luna offered a truce. Rudy pecked the mud from her face.

Luna yelled for help, but the animals were afraid of Luna. Rudy the Robin was afraid too, but he felt sorry for Luna.

Soon Luna came to the river. She saw Bruce's face in the water. Thinking Bruce was in the river, Luna jumped in. Luna swam and swam, trying to get to Bruce.

At last Luna dragged herself to the bank and fell asleep. Then Bruce played his rudest trick. He packed thick mud on Luna's face.

When Luna woke up, she could not see! The mud was dry and hard. Luna could not get it off.

SRAonline.com

Copyright © 2008 by SRA/McGraw-Hill.

Printed in the United States of America.

Send all inquiries to this address:
SRA/McGraw-Hill
4400 Easton Commons
Columbus, OH 43219

The McGraw-Hill Companies

SRA Decodable Stories

Drew's True Lesson

by Margaret Mason
illustrated by Rachel Ivanyi

Decodable Story 34

Columbus, OH

Peacock Hill Farm was a happy place. A nice breeze blew. Pretty peacocks strutted in the yard. Crows grew fat on the farmer's corn.

Drew learned a true lesson that day. He knew never to pretend to be something he was not.

He groomed his glossy black plumes.

After a while Drew said to the crows, "Did you know that peacocks can hardly fly? That's why they walk from here to there!"

Drew knew he was happy to be with his crew!

Not all those at Peacock Hill Farm were happy. While people praised the peacocks, Drew the crow grew tired of being ignored. Drew wanted to feel important, too.

Drew spotted a peacock plume speckled with dew. He admired its deep greens and dazzling blues. What would it be like…?

Drew gave the crows the "sorry" they were due. Slowly, Drew's crew forgave him, and Drew felt better.

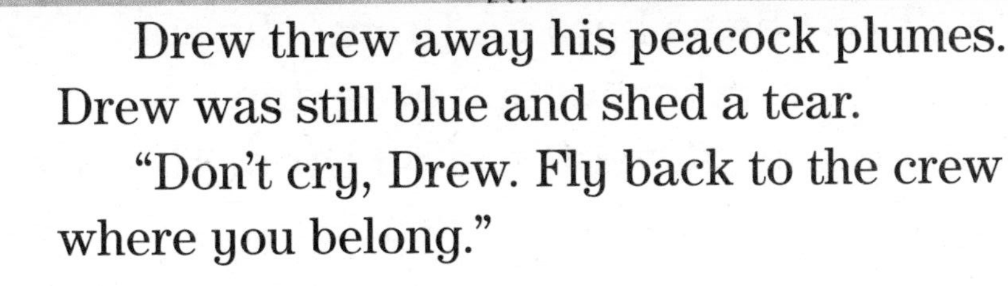

Drew threw away his peacock plumes.
Drew was still blue and shed a tear.

"Don't cry, Drew. Fly back to the crew where you belong."

In Drew's unhappy brain a plan was brewing. If only he could have a few peacock feathers.

Drew gathered the peacock's cast-offs.

On Tuesday Drew had new plumes and a tube of glue. Soon Drew was strutting like a peacock. He felt quite fancy!

Then a wise old crow spoke up.

"Don't be so hard on Drew," she said. "He made a mistake, but you have, too."

Then she flew off to find Drew. The crows knew that what she said was true.

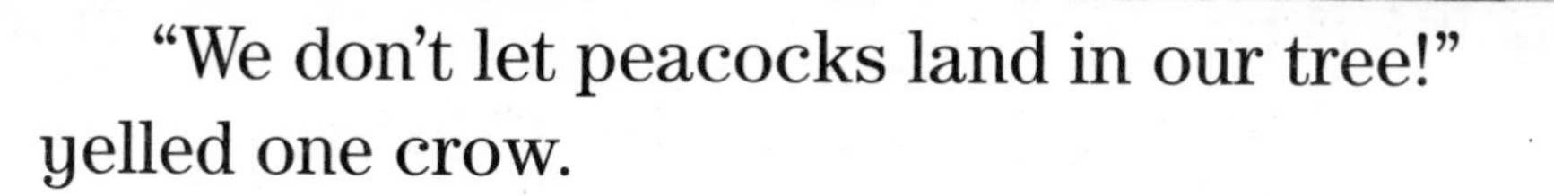

“We don’t let peacocks land in our tree!” yelled one crow.

“You don’t need us!” yelled another.

And so Drew flew sadly away.

A few crows spotted Drew.

“Drew thinks he’s a peacock! What a fool!”

“It does not matter what you think!” Drew told them. “I don’t need you plain old crows!”

Drew's new plan was to spend his days with the peacocks. But the peacocks had their own plans.

"You are not one of us!" they told him. "Go back to your own crew!"

Now Drew was sad and blue. He hung his head and heaved a sigh. Slowly Drew flew back to the crows' tree.

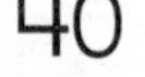

SRAonline.com

SRA

Printed in the United States of America.

Send all inquiries to this address:
SRA/McGraw-Hill
4400 Easton Commons
Columbus, OH 43219

The McGraw-Hill Companies

Look How Pets Adapt

by Sean Sanders
illustrated by Karen Tafoya

Decodable Story 35

SRA

Columbus, OH

Wild animals are good at adapting. They must adapt to survive and thrive. Life in the woods can be hard.

People help pets feel good and stay safe. At times, they help the animals in the woods, too.

Pets are part of the family. These two stood for the family photo!

Most pets do not have to look for food or work hard to survive. People help pets have easier lives. Still, pets are good at adapting to change.

Pets shed more when it is hot. These pets shook, and took off their coats! Their fur is now thinner, which helps them stay good and cool.

In winter, people provide warm homes for their pets. They may even have a hood and boots for the ice! Don't forget to hang them on the hook when you get back!

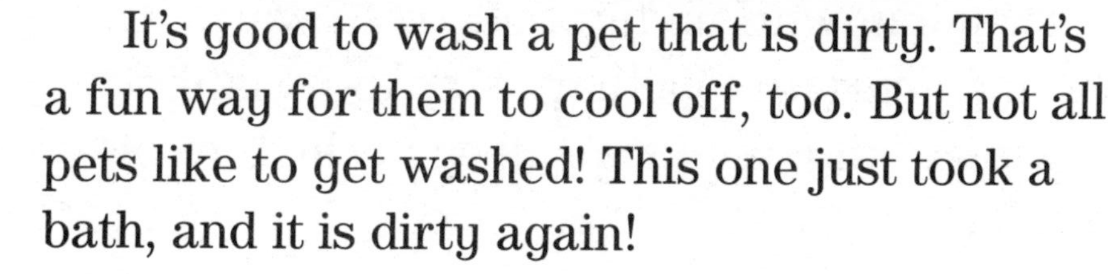

It's good to wash a pet that is dirty. That's a fun way for them to cool off, too. But not all pets like to get washed! This one just took a bath, and it is dirty again!

Pets may eat a good deal less when it's hot. You may note that they look thinner.

Pets are good at finding cool spots. A cat may look for a cool clay pot. A foot in a brook is even better!

They may curl up tightly to stay warm. Or, they may curl up together on a wool blanket! All winter long, they may sleep at the foot of your bed.

In winter, pets seek out warm places. They look for a spot of sun to nap in. They may look for a cozy nook by a book.

Pets may hide from the heat beneath a wood porch. They may lie under a hood. These pets stood beside the fan all day!

When it is cool, pets change their ways. Just as you may put on a wool coat to stay warm, their fur thickens to make a winter coat. They shed a good deal less, too.

They may look for more food to eat. Plenty of food helps animals stay warm. Do your pets beg when you cook good food?

SRAonline.com

Printed in the United States of America.

Send all inquiries to this address:
SRA/McGraw-Hill
4400 Easton Commons
Columbus, OH 43219

The McGraw-Hill Companies

Mr. Brown Sees the World

by Ethan Rodriguez
illustrated by John Edwards

Decodable Story 36

Columbus, OH

Mr. Brown had never traveled far from his home. He wanted to have a look about and see the world.

Mr. Brown went out and had quite a trip! He got to see the world, and the world got to see Mr. Brown!

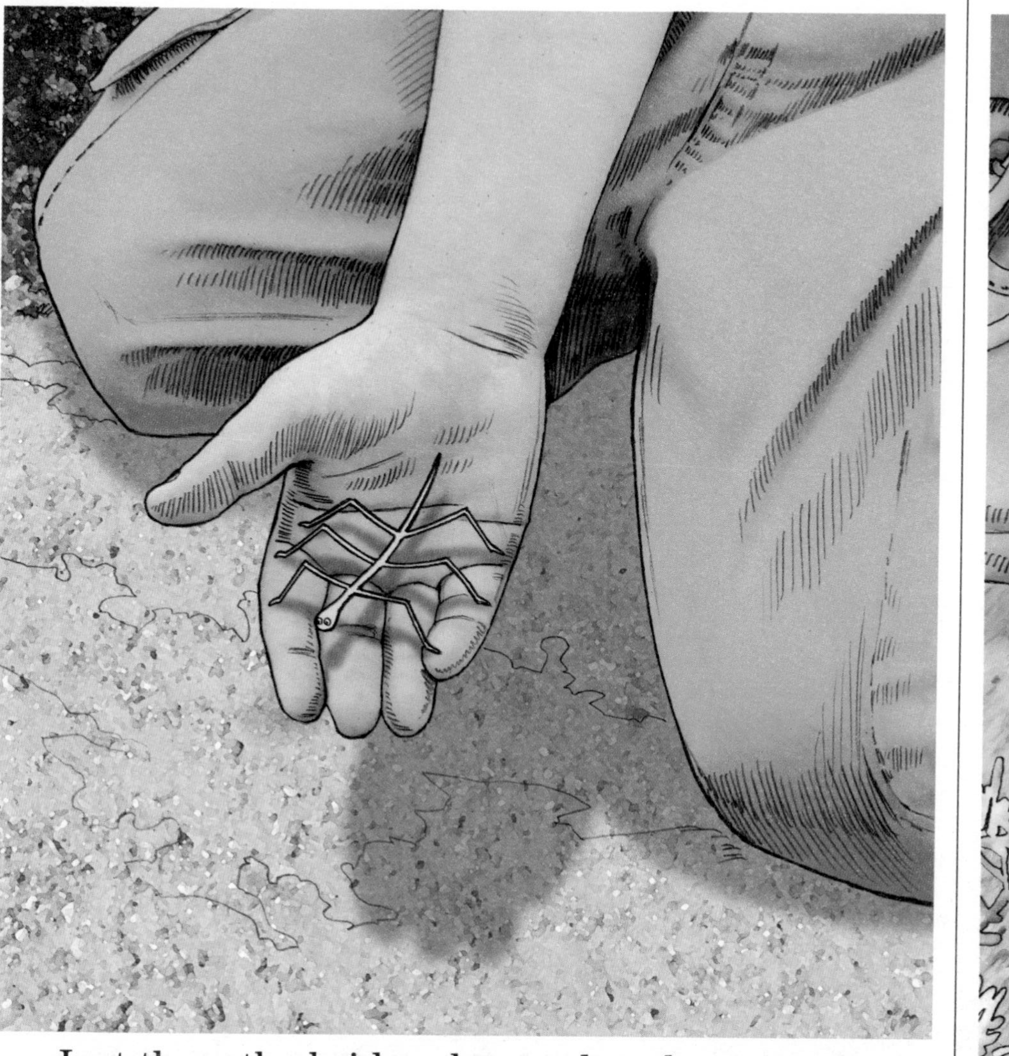

Just then, the bridge dropped to the ground. Mr. Brown took a quick look around and found his way home.

Mr. Brown set out, and right away he found a rock. He climbed up and took a look around.

At the top of the rock Mr. Brown found a round brown thing.

"I will climb to the top of this tree," Mr. Brown decided.

Mr. Brown climbed up.

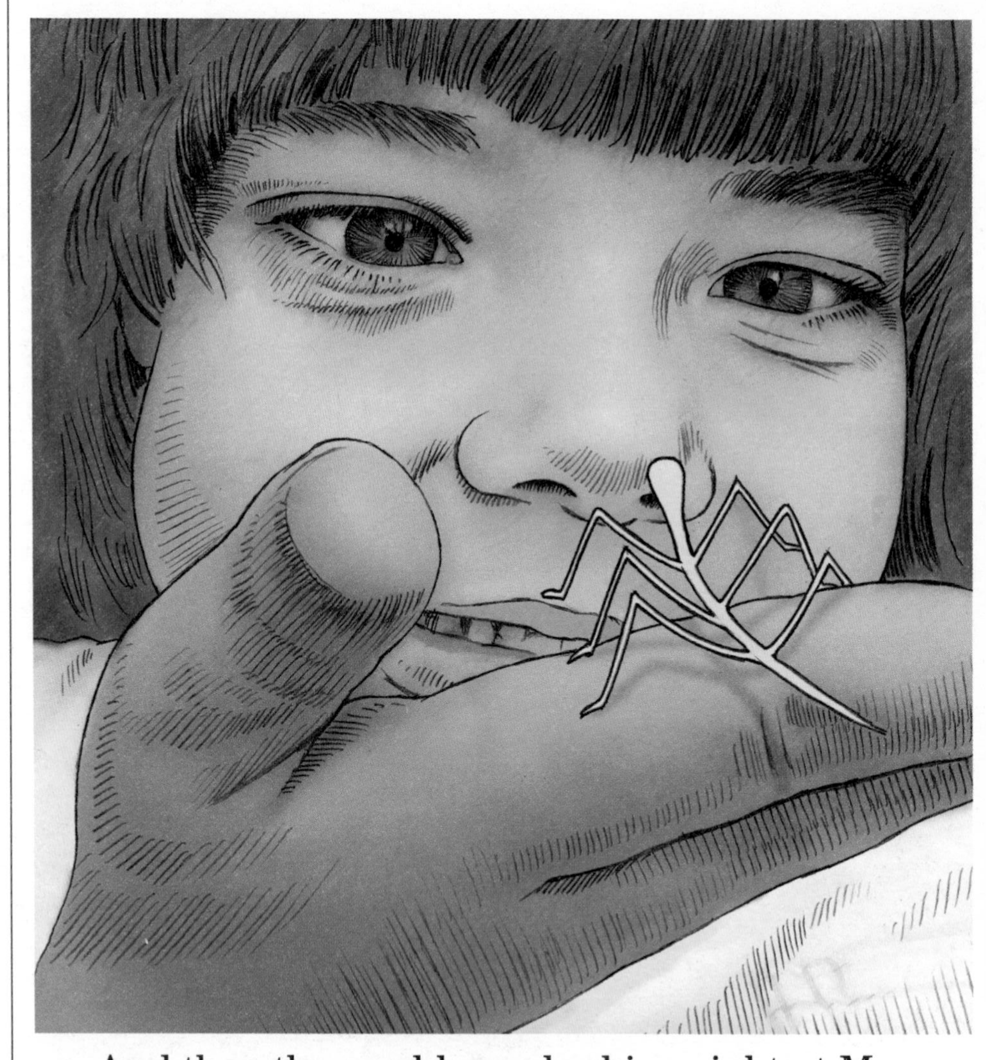

And then the world was looking right at Mr. Brown and making some sort of sound. Who knew that the world had a mouth?

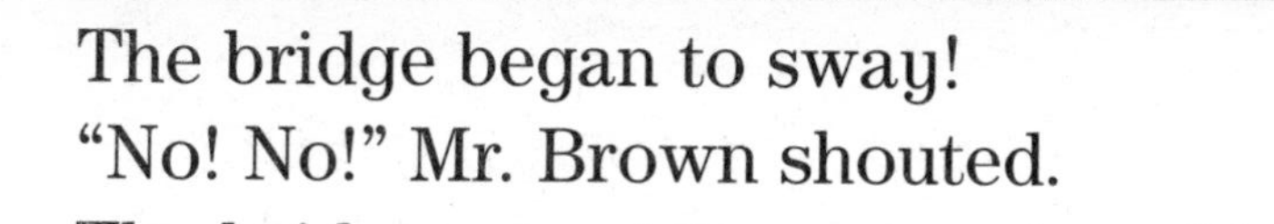

The bridge began to sway!

"No! No!" Mr. Brown shouted.

The bridge was rising up and up, higher and higher. Mr. Brown was sorry he ever wanted to prowl.

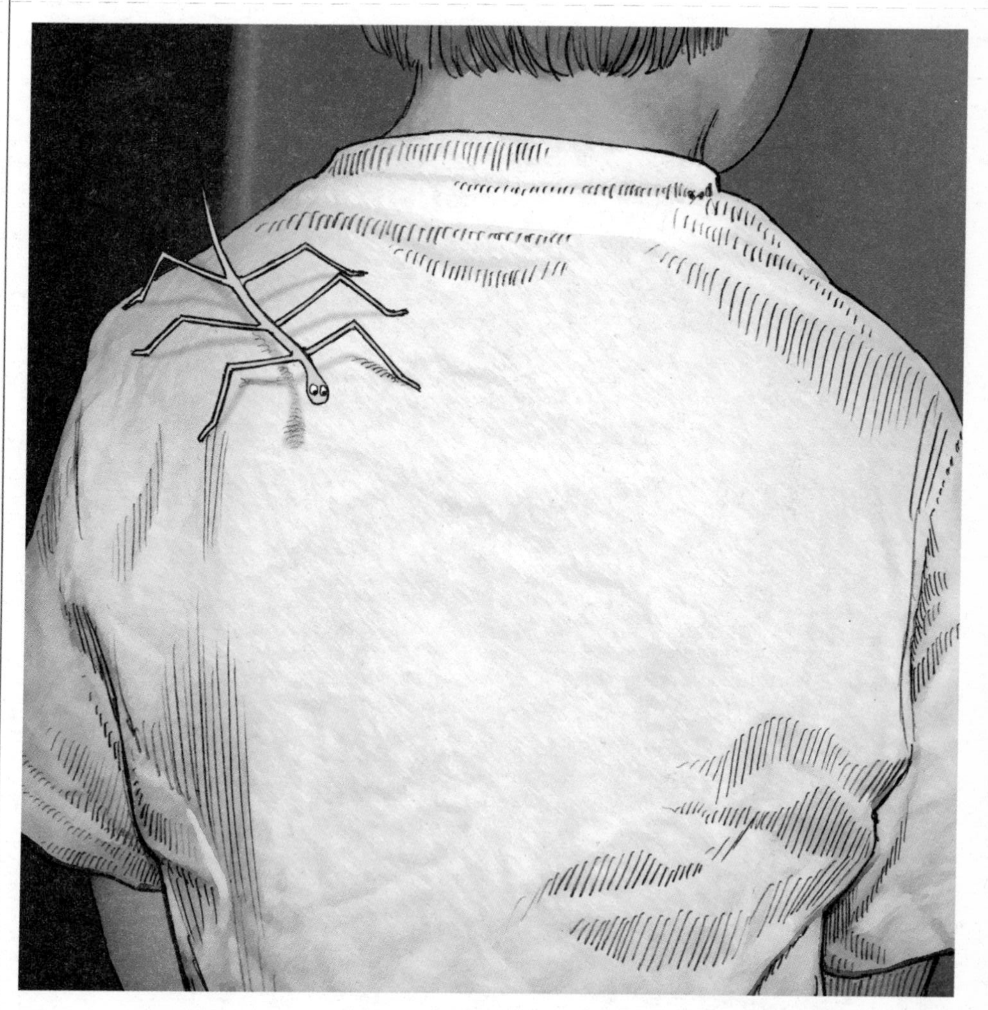

At last he came to a soft white object.

"How did I get up in the clouds? How will I get down?"

Mr. Brown had another look around.

Mr. Brown made his way across the cloud. Suddenly there was a loud sound. The cloud shook.

"It must be a storm," Mr. Brown said.

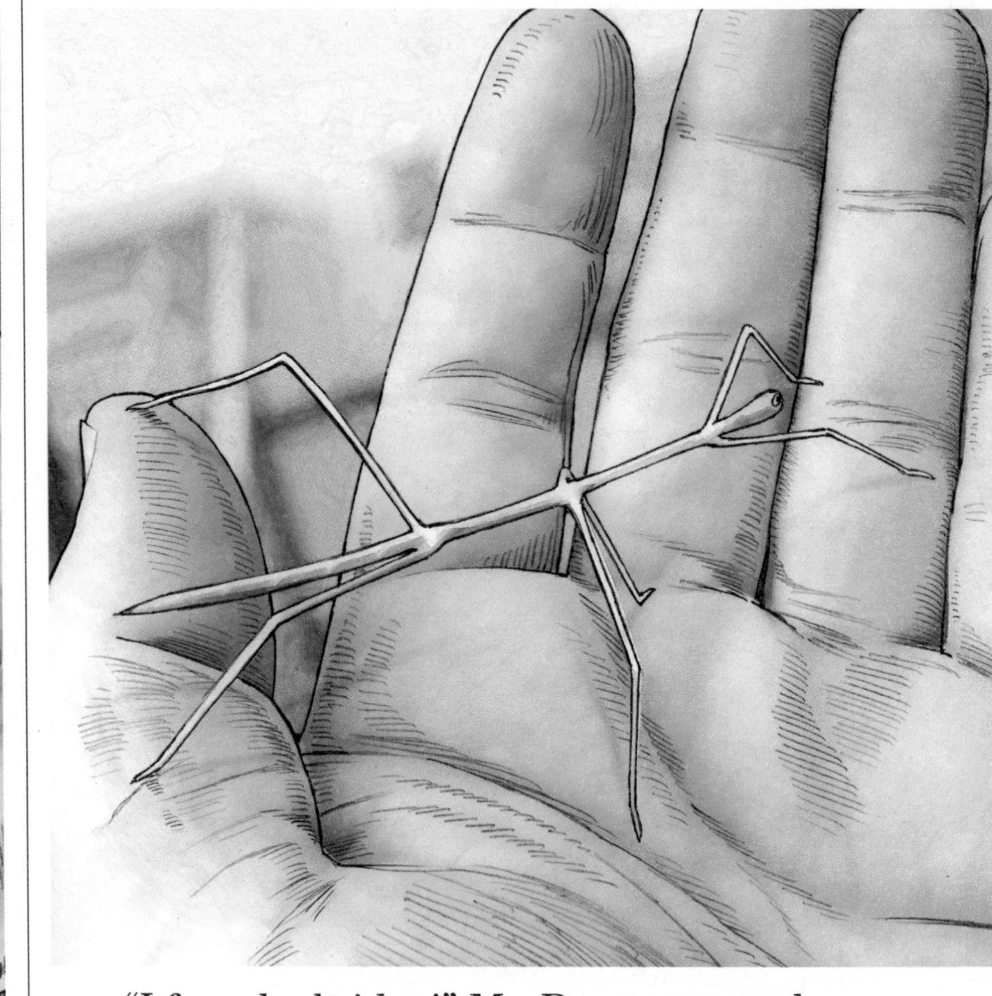

"I found a bridge!" Mr. Brown gasped.

The land was very narrow now. The bridge suddenly ended, but Mr. Brown did not have room to turn around. He was about to panic when…

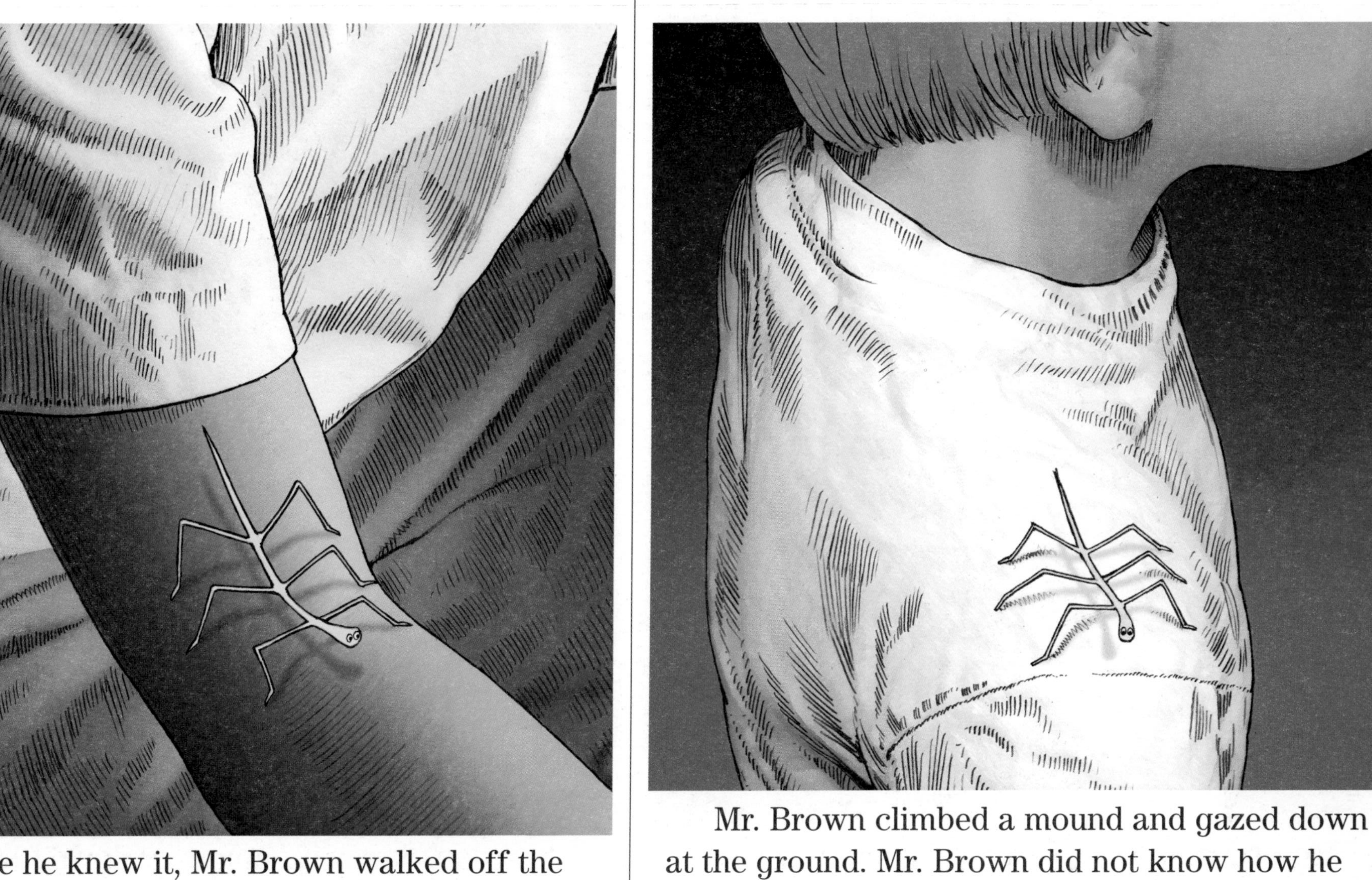

Before he knew it, Mr. Brown walked off the cloud back down to the ground. He walked down to a valley and then back up.

74

Mr. Brown climbed a mound and gazed down at the ground. Mr. Brown did not know how he would ever get home. Mr. Brown frowned, looked around, and kept going.

71

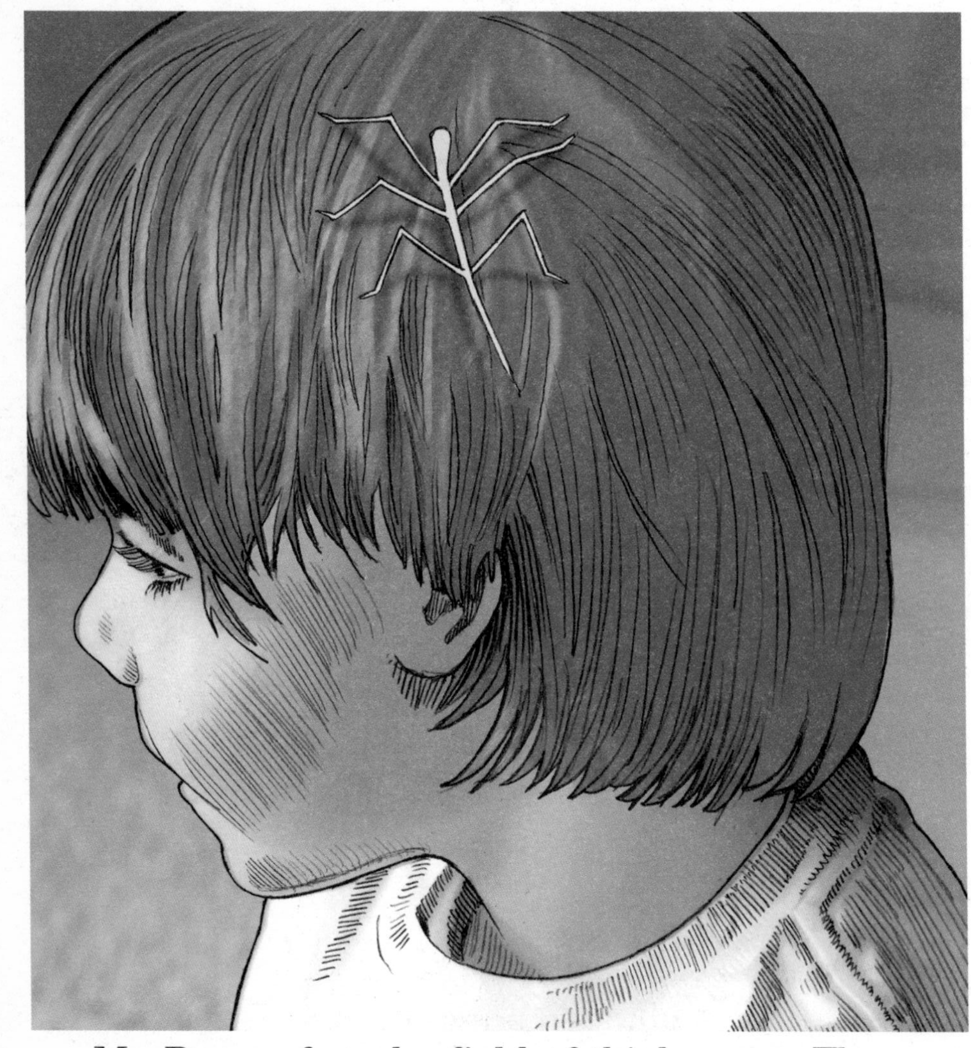

Mr. Brown found a field of thick grass. The grass swayed in the breeze. Mr. Brown pretended to be a brave scout and walked into the field.

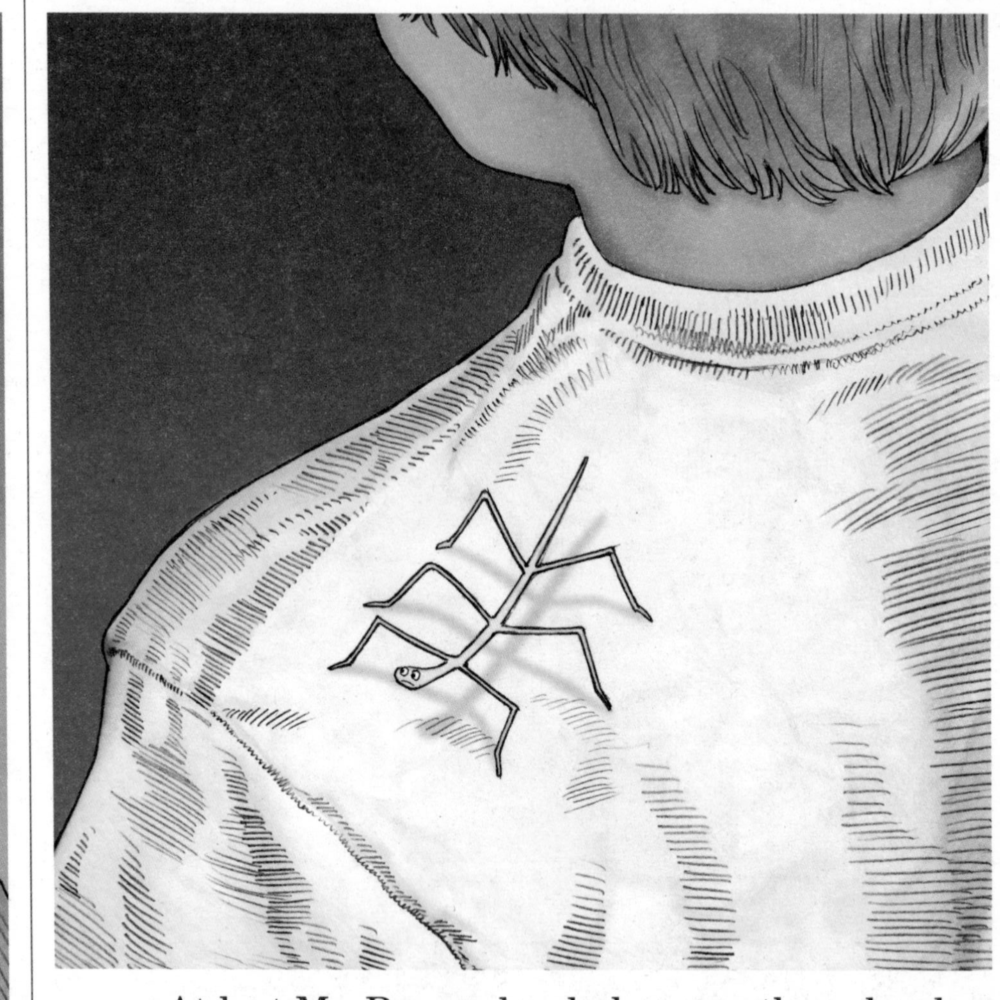

At last Mr. Brown landed on another cloud.

"I don't know if I am up or down!" he said. "This land is mighty odd, with grass and clouds mixed in."

SRAonline.com

Printed in the United States of America.

Send all inquiries to this address:
SRA/McGraw-Hill
4400 Easton Commons
Columbus, OH 43219

The McGraw-Hill Companies

A Plant that Acts Like an Animal

by Elizabeth Ramsey
illustrated by Dave Fischer

Decodable Story 37

Columbus, OH

Like animals, plants adapt to their surroundings. One such plant is the Venus flytrap. It grows in bogs and marshes.

- Plant flytrap in a mix of peat moss and sand.
- Add water to keep roots wet.
- Jar keeps dampness in.
- Don't forget to give your flytrap food!

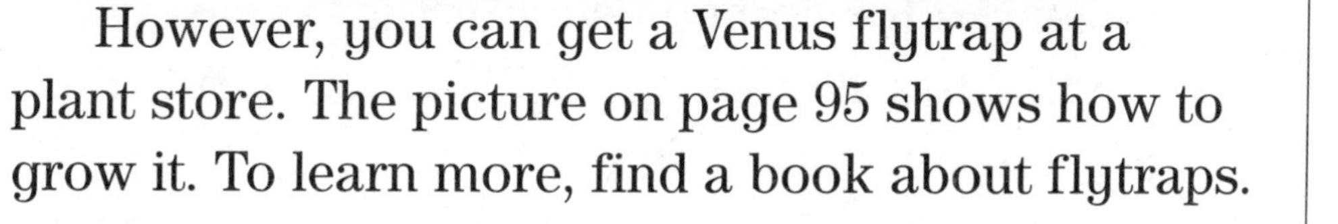

However, you can get a Venus flytrap at a plant store. The picture on page 95 shows how to grow it. To learn more, find a book about flytraps.

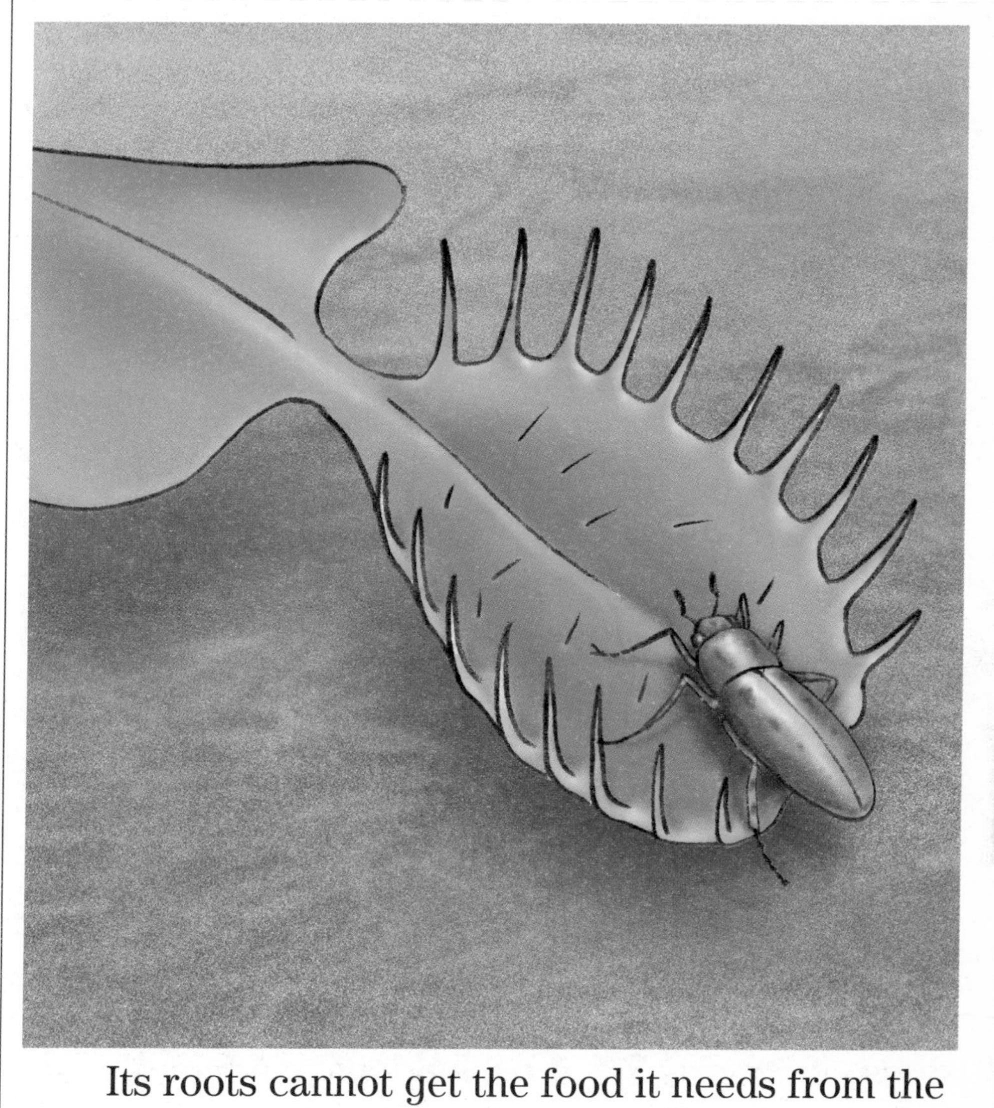

Its roots cannot get the food it needs from the marsh. So the Venus flytrap eats bugs. This plant truly acts like an animal!

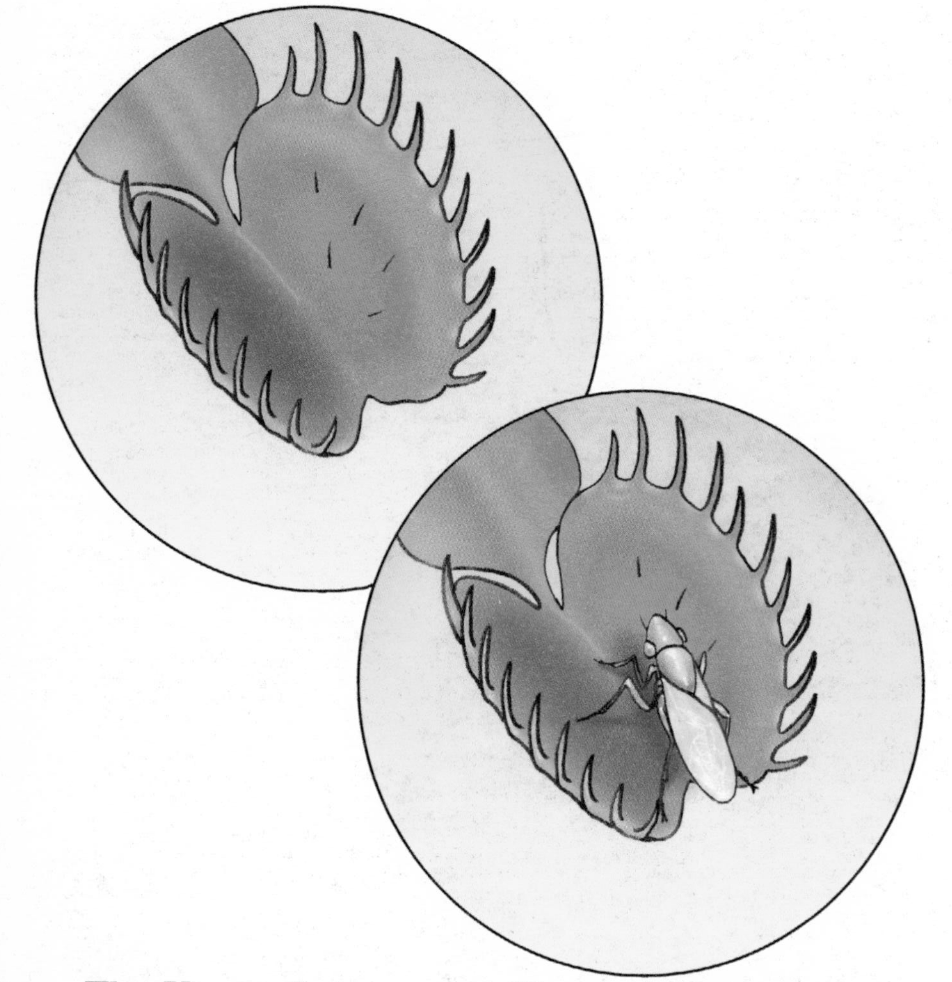

The Venus flytrap eats flies, crickets, spiders, slugs, and more. Yet, it does not have a mouth and cannot chew. The pictures on these pages show how a plant can eat.

Some marshes and bogs are dirty. Some have been cleared for human use. For these reasons, wild flytraps are endangered. Now, it's a rule that people can no longer dig them up.

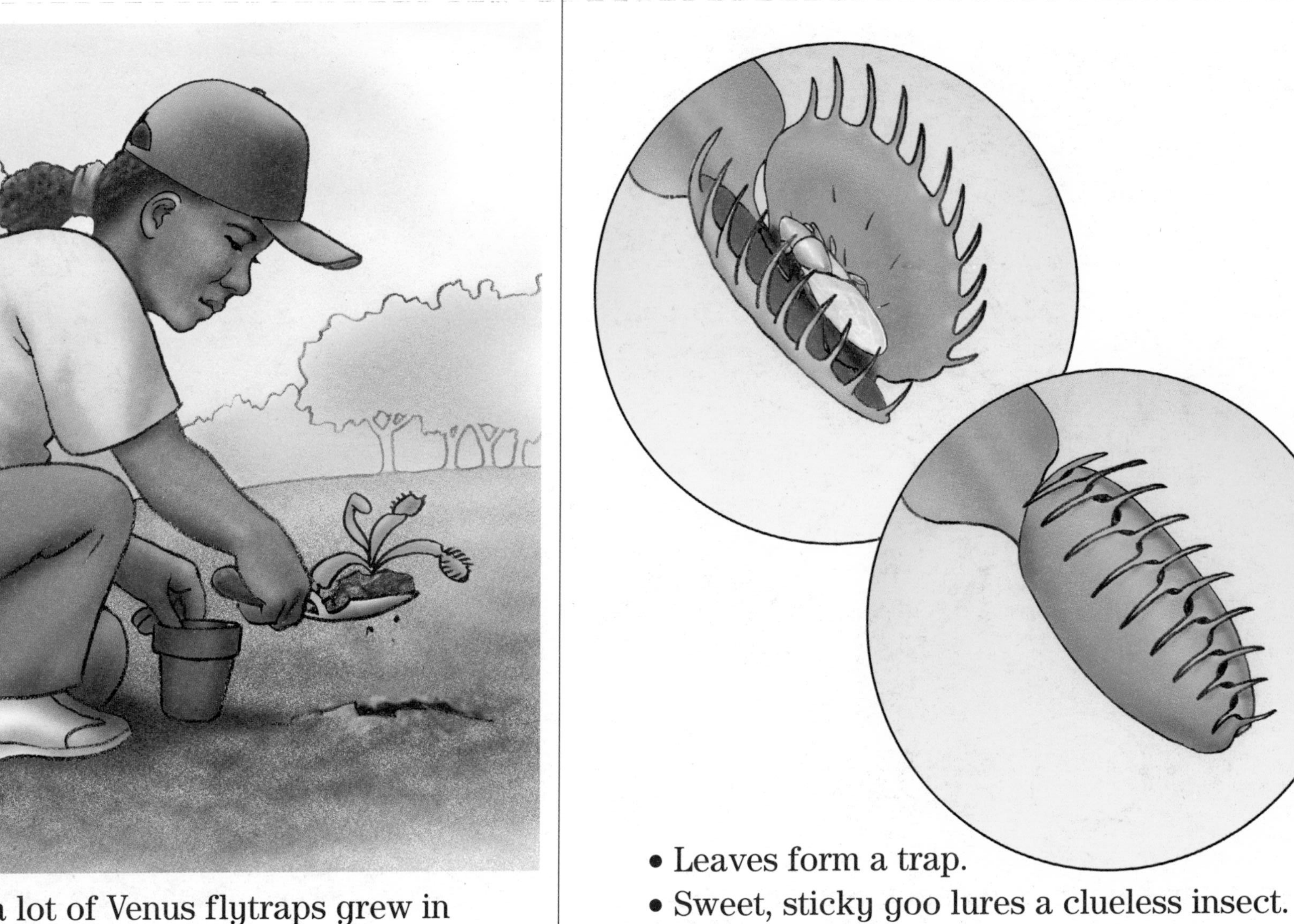

In the past, a lot of Venus flytraps grew in the wild. Now, few are left there. Over the years, people took many of them home.

- Leaves form a trap.
- Sweet, sticky goo lures a clueless insect.
- "Trigger hairs" make the trap snap shut.
- The insect is doomed. It cannot get out.

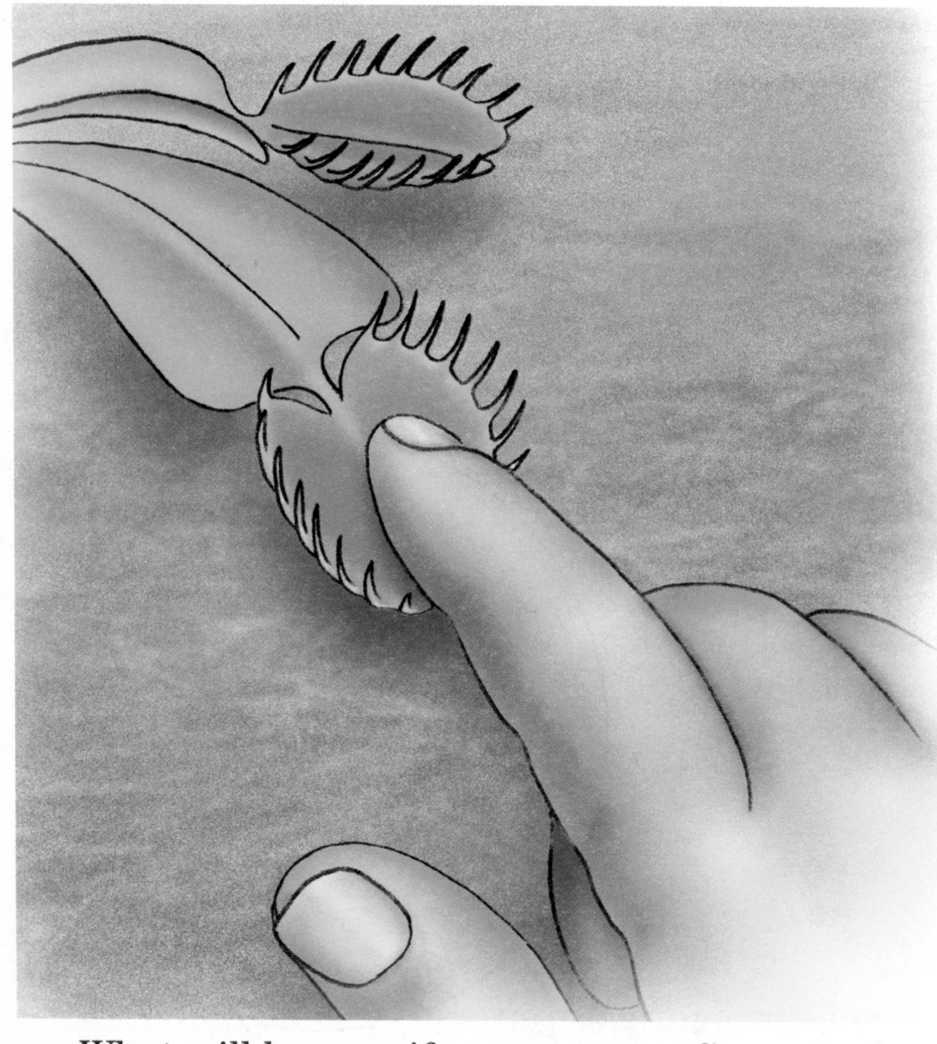

What will happen if you put your finger in the trap? The flytrap will not be fooled. The trap will close part of the way and then open again.

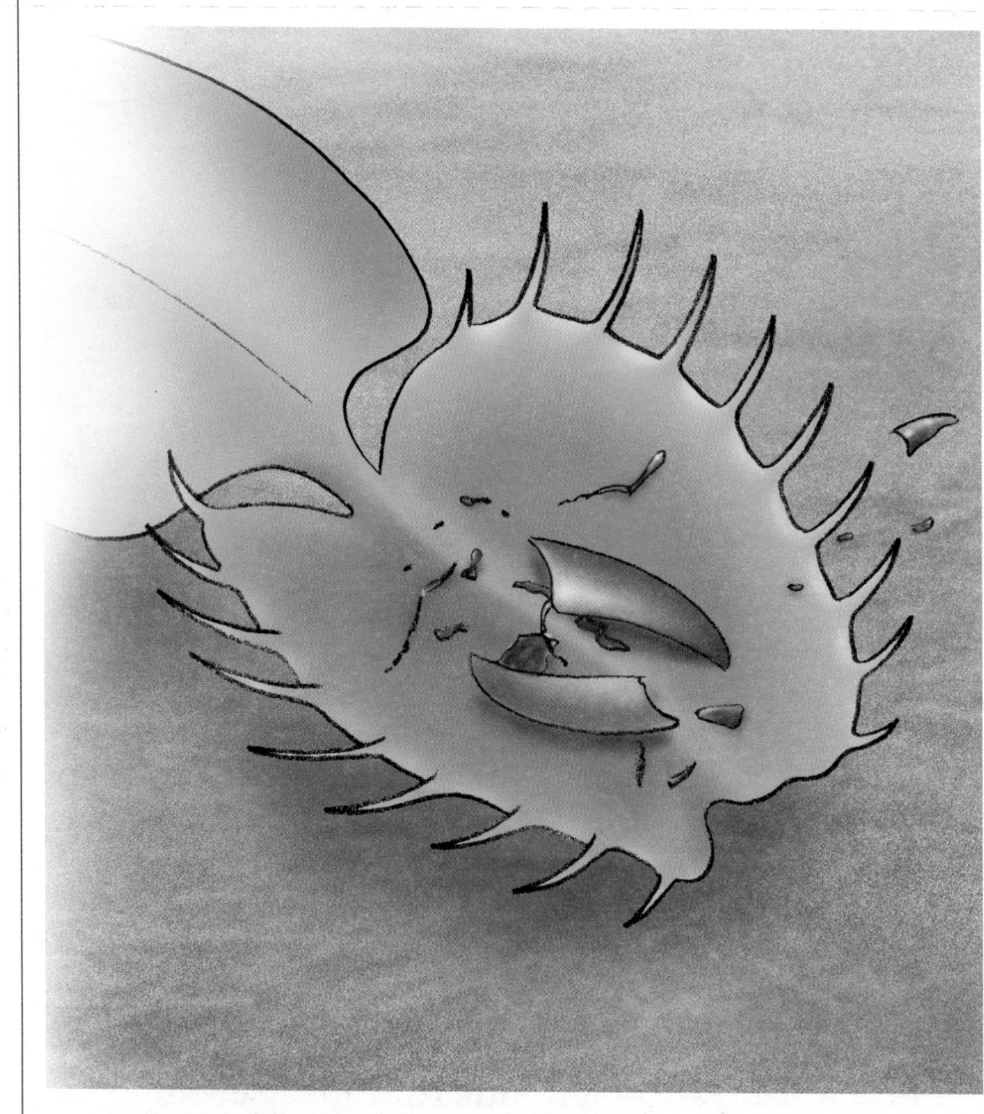

Then, the trap opens. Look at what is left of the bug! Rain or wind will carry this away.

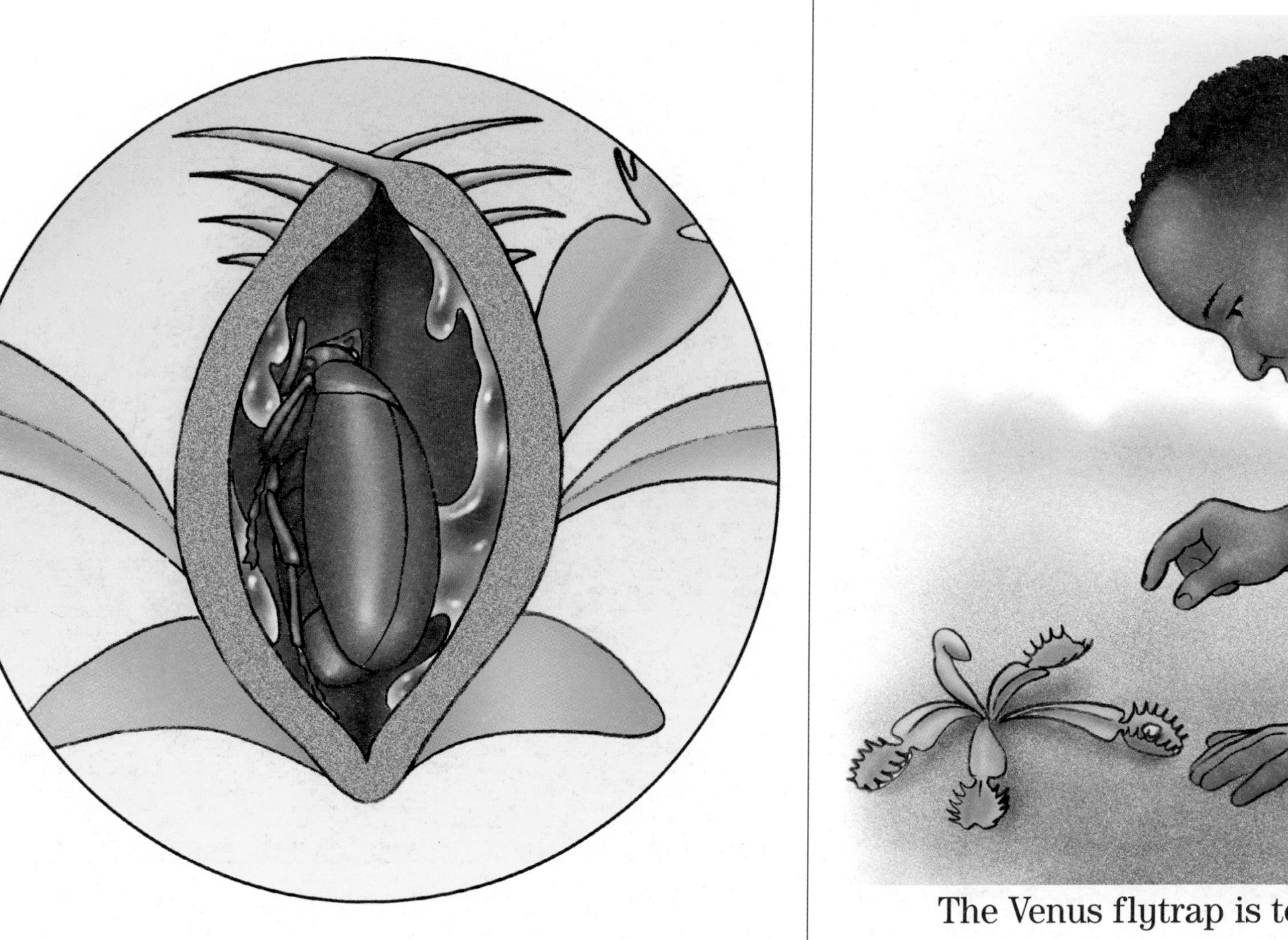

When the trap closes, however, it's dinner time! Acid oozes into the trap. This acid lets the plant digest the bug. It may take a week or more.

The Venus flytrap is too smart to pounce on your finger. It will not chow down on a pebble or a twig either. It can tell that those things are not food!

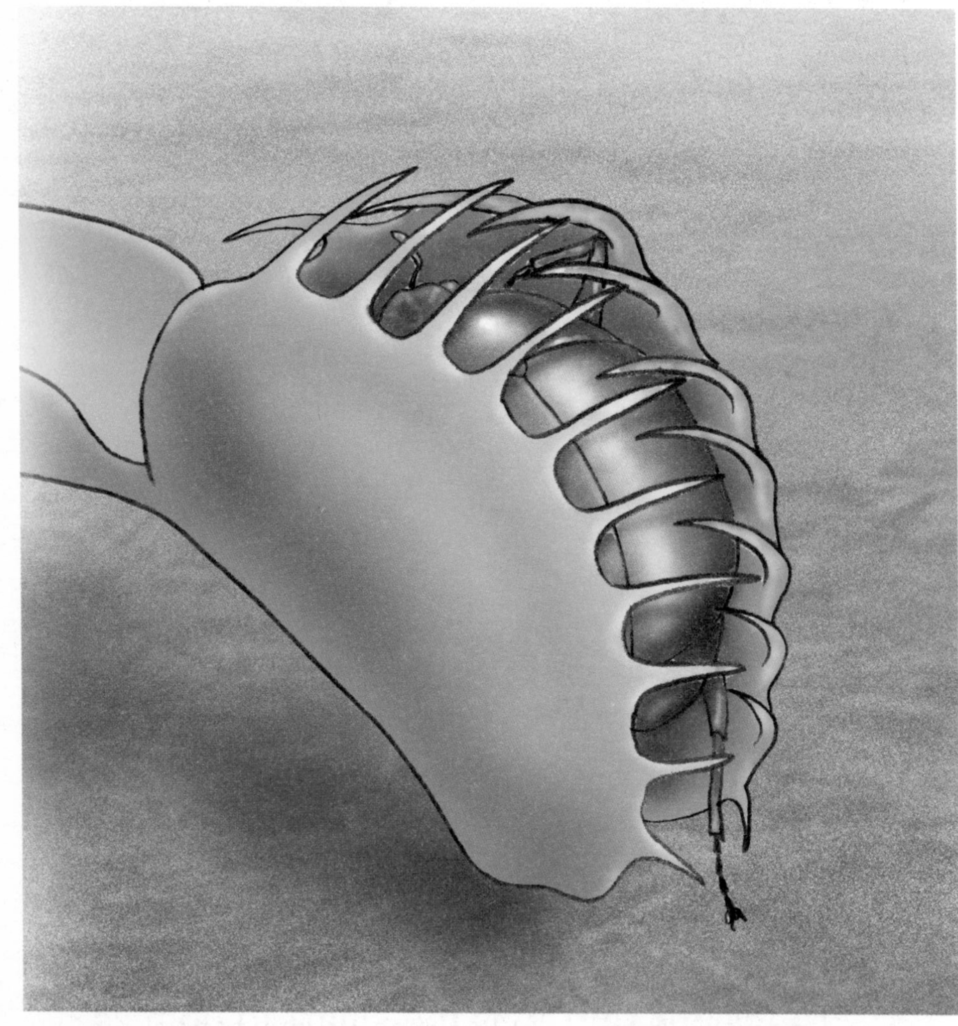

The Venus flytrap cannot eat large insects. Each trap is only about an inch long. The trap must be able to close and make an airtight pouch.

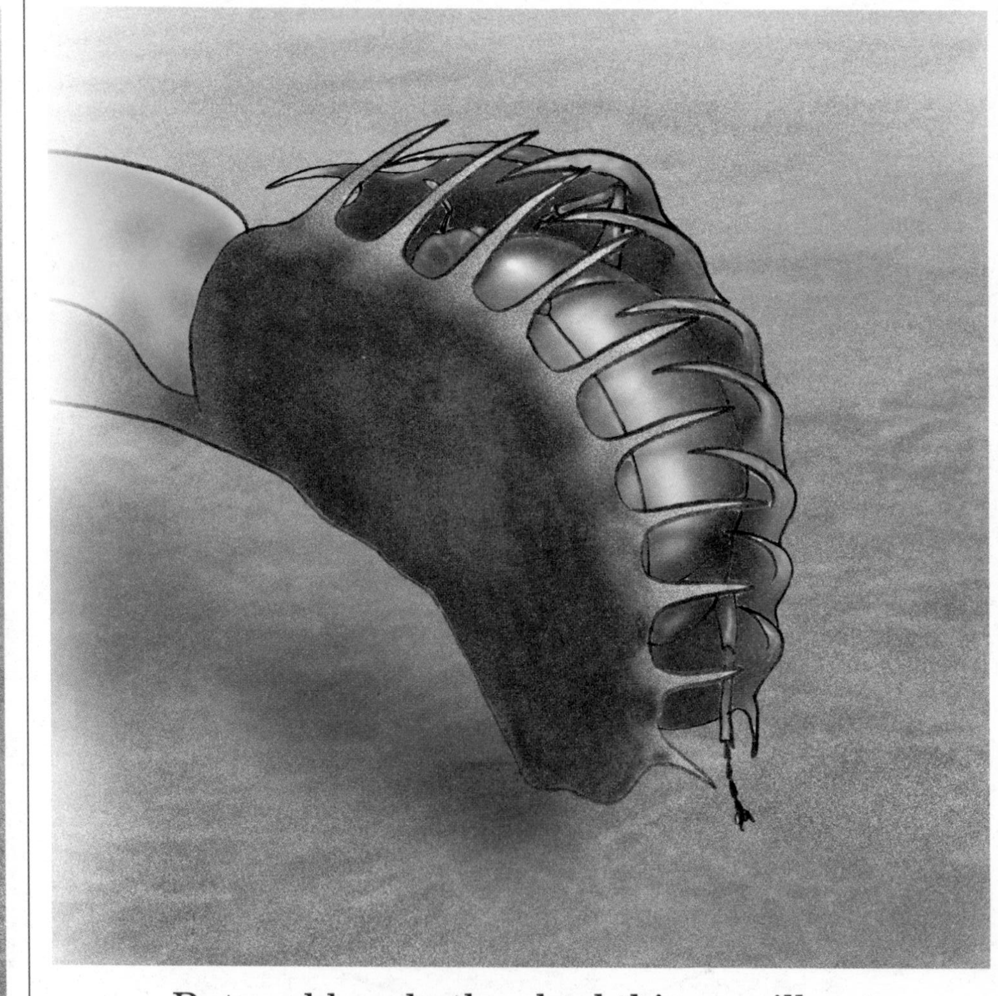

But mold and other bad things will enter the trap. The trap may droop, turn brown, and drop from the plant. In that case, the plant will grow a new trap.

SRAonline.com

Printed in the United States of America.

Send all inquiries to this address:
SRA/McGraw-Hill
4400 Easton Commons
Columbus, OH 43219

The McGraw-Hill Companies

Animal Expert in Outer Space

by Sean Sanders
illustrated by Karen Tafoya

Decodable Story 38

Columbus, OH

"Hello, kids, and thanks for tuning in. In the past, the crew of *Animal Expert* has traveled around the globe. We have shown you how animals adapt to their surroundings."

"Look, Sue, it's a zebra from Stripe! What's that doing down here on Earth?"

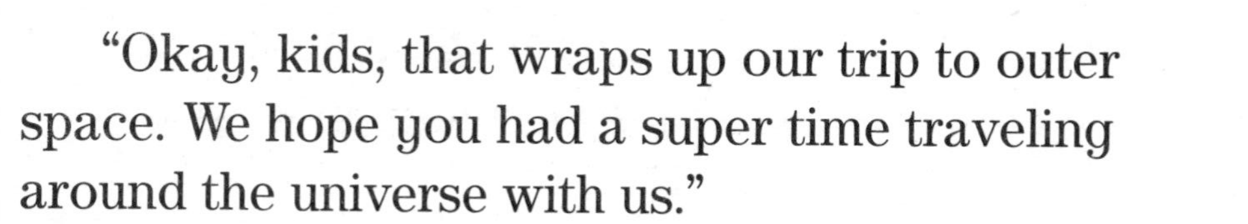

"Okay, kids, that wraps up our trip to outer space. We hope you had a super time traveling around the universe with us."

"This week's show is beyond the globe. That's right! Our search for interesting animals will take us to outer space! Do animals in outer space adapt as those on Earth do? Let's find out!"

“Our first stop in outer space is to a place named Dot. Let’s see how many animals we can spot on Dot! Cooper, what are you looking at over there?”

“Well, Sue, there’s a blue fowl on your head. And a cool blue animal is climbing up your leg!”

"Here we are at our last stop, a place named Blue. We're deep in the Blue Woods. It's full of blue trees and blue flowers with blue blooms. Cooper, what animals are in the Blue Woods?"

"Sue, this is a dotted blue goon. I had seen them in pictures, but this is the first one I've seen in the wild.

"Is the microphone picking up that low growl? That sound is what allowed me to find it. See how well it blends in with its home?"

"Here we are at a place named Round. Wow! Everything is round! I don't see many animals around, however. What about you, Cooper?"

"Yes there are, Sue. Look closely at the sand dunes in back of us. Some of those dunes are space hounds. They are sleeping now, but when the full moon rises, look out!"

"Now here is a place that I've been hoping to visit. This is Three. Let me tell you kids, there are triangles everywhere I look!"

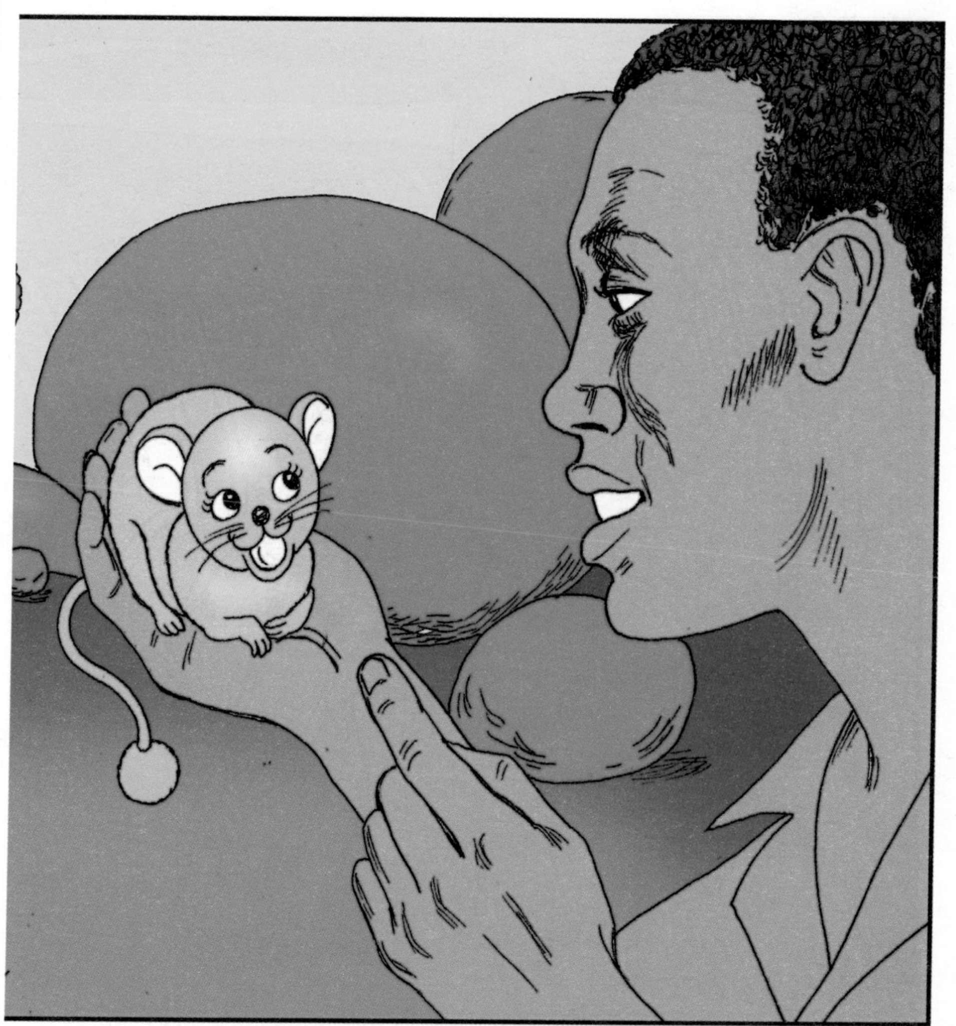

"Well, Sue, you must look really well. You see, most of the animals here are round, too! Look, I'm holding a round mouse. See his big round tooth?"

"That's interesting, Cooper. Now we are visiting another far-out place. Here on Stripe, the animals have stripes, as you might think by now."

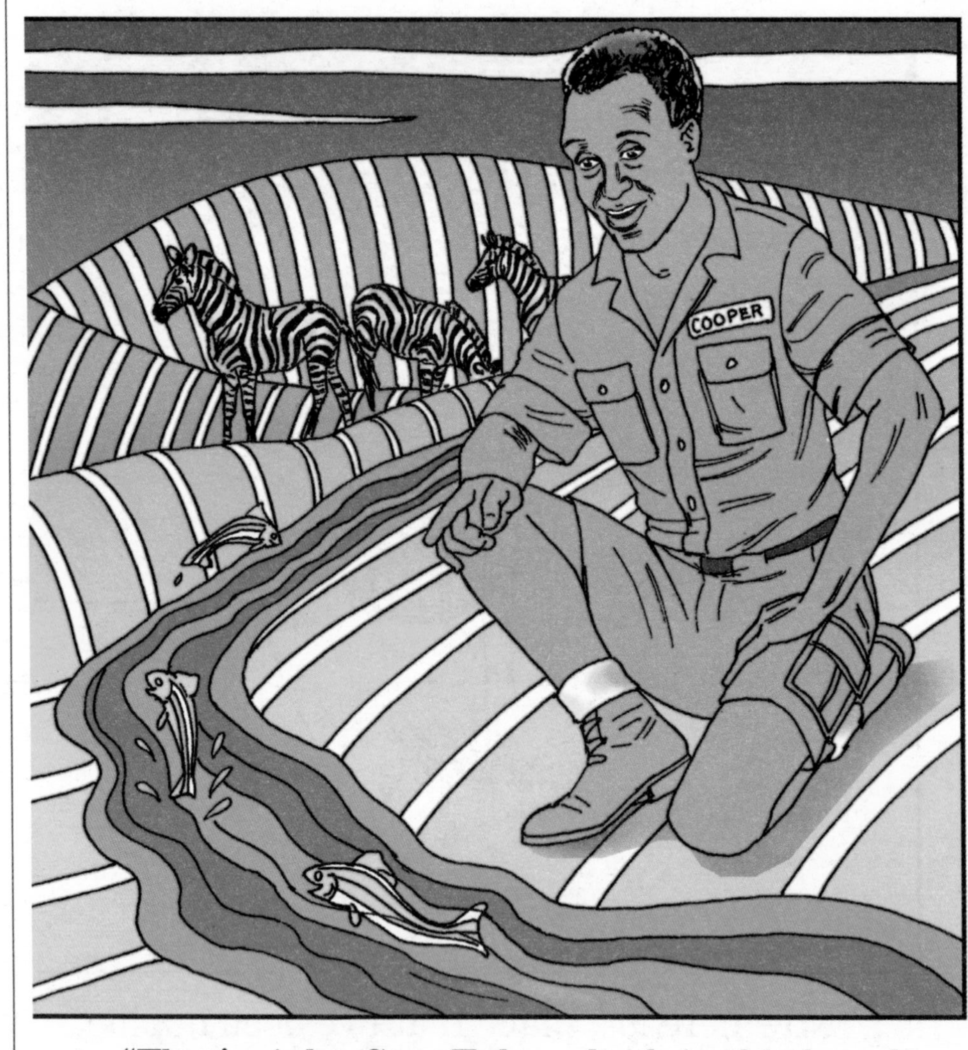

"That's right, Sue. Take a look in this brook. It's full of striped trout. And over there is a striped zebra!"

SRAonline.com

Printed in the United States of America.

Send all inquiries to this address:
SRA/McGraw-Hill
4400 Easton Commons
Columbus, OH 43219

The McGraw-Hill Companies

SRA Decodable Stories

The Lion and the Mouse

as retold by Margaret Mason
illustrated by Linda Bronson

Decodable Story 39

Columbus, OH

Lack of fear is not the same as bravery.
In fact, a lack of fear can be foolish.
In this story, Mouse learns how they are different.

*　*　*

It was a peaceful August afternoon in the jungle. Mighty Lion was napping. Playful Mouse was out for a run.

Now, Mouse had a fault. He liked to take silly risks. He felt this made him brave. In truth, it simply made him foolish.

Mouse paused and heard Lion snoring. He chose to tease the beast. *Lion may be big and brawny,* he told himself, *but I'm faster.*

Mouse kept away from Lion. Then, one autumn day at dawn, he heard Lion roaring for help. Mouse ran to the awful sound.

He saw Lion trapped in a net.

"Draw near and help me!" ordered Lion.

"But I said I'd never come near you!" protested Mouse.

"I didn't hurt you when you acted foolish," said Lion. "I will not hurt you for helping me now."

Shaking with fear, Mouse crawled to the net. He chewed it apart. Lion jumped out.

"Thank you, Mouse," said Lion. "You showed real bravery."

"I learned bravery from you, Lion," said Mouse. "I used to think I was brave when I had no fear. But now I know real bravery is helping even when I am scared."

6

3

Mouse scampered across Lion's paw. That didn't wake Lion, so Mouse continued to play. He crawled all over Lion and then launched himself right onto Lion's nose!

In a flash, Lion woke up. He smacked Mouse with his paw and trapped him under a claw.

"I was just dreaming of a snack," Lion said with a yawn.

Lion hauled Mouse up and looked at him closely.

"Mighty Lion, please don't eat me!" bawled Mouse as he looked at Lion's jaws.

"Why not?" asked Lion.

"Because I would taste awful," said Mouse, trembling. "And, I learned a lesson. I'll never bother you again."

"Go, then," said Lion. "You're too scrawny. I need a bigger meal. But never draw near me again."

SRAonline.com

SRA

Printed in the United States of America.

Send all inquiries to this address:
SRA/McGraw-Hill
4400 Easton Commons
Columbus, OH 43219

The McGraw-Hill Companies

The Bootmaker's Daughter

by Ethan Rodriguez
illustrated by Linda Bronson

Decodable Story 40

SRA

Columbus, OH

9

It takes bravery to right a wrong.
Many times, it takes intelligence.
In this story, a bootmaker's daughter uses both.

* * *

Long ago, a bootmaker and his daughter lived in a small city. The bootmaker was called Walt. His daughter was Jenny.

One day, Walt took all his boots to the city in his cart. Walt passed the stall of a rich merchant.

"Halt!" cried the merchant. "How much for all you have?"

"Ten gold pieces," Walt said.

The merchant paid Walt ten gold pieces. Then the merchant got into the cart and told Walt to get out.

"Why should I get out of my cart?" asked Walt.

The merchant gave Jenny the gold.

"And your three gold rings," Jenny said.

"What?" cried the merchant.

"You offered me all that was in your hand," said Jenny. "Take off those rings, or I'll call the judge!"

"Let the judge rule, then!" said the merchant.

"You ought to be clearer," said the judge. "Give her those rings."

The merchant was caught in his own trap. He handed Jenny the rings. She kept two and held up the smallest.

"Will you trade this for Walt's horse and cart?" Jenny asked.

"You're Walt's daughter!" gasped the merchant. They traded and Jenny rode home.

"I taught that naughty merchant a lesson!" Jenny told Walt.

"You agreed to sell all," said the tricky merchant. "That includes the cart and horse. I bought it all. It's mine. Ask the judge!"

Walt sought the judge and told his story.

"You ought to be clearer," said the judge. "I cannot help you."

Walt walked slowly home and told Jenny all.

"Don't cry," said Jenny. "I have a thought. Make more boots!"

A week later, Jenny took the new boots to town in a small wheelbarrow. The rich merchant ran from his stall.

"How much for all you've brought?" he asked.

"How much will you offer?" Jenny countered.

He held out three gold pieces.

"You offer all that's in your hand?" Jenny asked.

"Yes," agreed the merchant.

SRAonline.com

Printed in the United States of America.

Send all inquiries to this address:
SRA/McGraw-Hill
4400 Easton Commons
Columbus, OH 43219

The McGraw-Hill Companies

SRA Decodable Stories

Kim and the Wave

by Sean Saunders
illustrated by Lina Bronson

Decodable Story 41

Columbus, OH

Just then a mighty roar began. A huge wave, as high as a cliff, crashed over the town. The people saw it all from the hilltop.

"We were wrong to laugh at the leader's daughter," a man said. "She saved us even when we laughed at her."

After that day, no one laughed at Kim or called her bossy.

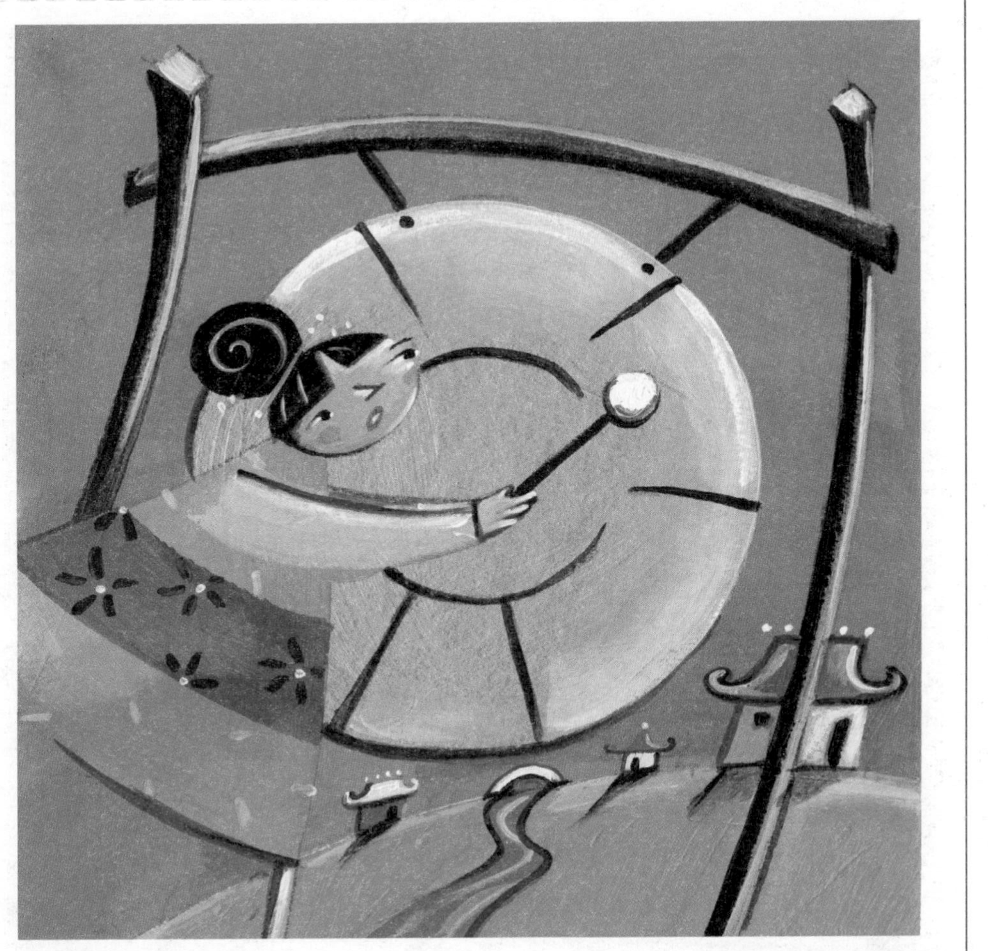

Kim struck the gong with all her might. Soon, all the people were running up the hill. When everyone was on the hilltop, a child cried, "I saw the leader's daughter ring the gong!"

"Kim, is it true?" her dad asked.

It takes bravery to do what is right.
This is most true when people laugh at you.
In this tale, a girl's bravery saves her town.

* * *

The town lay by the sea next to a high hill. Kim was the daughter of the town leader. Kim was smart and learned much from her family.

Kim liked to tell people all the stuff she knew, but the people in her town thought she was bossy. They laughed at her. Being the leader's daughter did not help matters.

Kim spent most days playing alone. One day, she was playing on the hilltop when she felt a small earthquake. Kim was used to such things. Still, she had a bad feeling.

Kim caught sight of the sea. It was racing away from the shore. Her granddad had said:

When the sea runs backwards, run up the hill. A huge wave is about to wash over the town.

Kim ran to tell the people in town.

She screamed, "Run up the hill! A huge wave is coming!"

They didn't understand what Kim meant. Some just laughed. How could Kim know a big wave is coming?

"Stop bossing us around."

"You're not our leader. You're just the leader's daughter!"

Kim had to save them. She ran to the town's gong. Only the leader was allowed to ring it. It meant that the people must gather on the hilltop to hear the leader speak.

SRAonline.com

Printed in the United States of America.

Send all inquiries to this address:
SRA/McGraw-Hill
4400 Easton Commons
Columbus, OH 43219

The McGraw-Hill Companies

How Roy Got a Toy Drum

by Elizabeth Ramsey
illustrated by Valeria Cis

Decodable Story 42

Columbus, OH

Next Roy met the baker. He had no bread to sell.

"I have flour but no oil," he said.

"Without oil, I cannot make bread."

Roy gave him the oil. The baker held out a sheet of shiny foil.

"Do you want this?"

"Yes, please!" said Roy.

Roy shaped the foil into a glittering toy. Soon an old man came along.

"I want that toy for my granddaughter," he said.

"Will you accept this coin for it?"

Roy raced to the store. He pointed at the toy drum and showed the seller his coin. At last, the toy drum was his! With joy, Roy joined a band.

Later, Roy told his mom this story.

"You put your own sadness aside and helped people," she said. "And in the end, your bravery paid off."

Keeping your chin up in hard times is one kind of bravery. In this tale, a boy cannot get the toy he wants. Instead of feeling sad, he always helps people.

* * *

Roy was a boy who lived with his mom. Roy's mom worked hard in the soil to grow food. She could not afford a toy drum for Roy.

Roy's mom wanted to get Roy the toy drum. But she didn't have a single coin.

Walking home, she found a coil of rope.

"It's not much," she thought, "but I'll give this to Roy."

Roy thanked his mom for the coil of rope.

"Thanks. It's nice of you to think of me," Roy said.

Soon he met the potter, who was yelling at his goat.

"What's wrong?" asked Roy.

"I need a rope to tie this goat. She always runs off."

Roy gave the potter his coil of rope. The happy potter gave Roy a pot.

Next Roy met a lady with children. The crying children were making an awful noise.

"What's wrong?" asked Roy.

"They are hungry," the lady said.

"I have rice but no pot to boil it in."

Roy gave her his pot.

"Take this oil," the lady said.

"I have too much, and it will spoil."

SRAonline.com

SRA

Printed in the United States of America.

Send all inquiries to this address:
SRA/McGraw-Hill
4400 Easton Commons
Columbus, OH 43219

The McGraw-Hill Companies

The Koi at the Dragon Gate

by Sean Saunders
illustrated by Valeria Cis

Decodable Story 43

SRA

Columbus, OH

It takes bravery to try something difficult. Yet, if you do not try, you may miss out on life's biggest joys.

* * *

In the East, there is a deep, salty sea. All kinds of fish live there, including koi. Mighty dragons live in the deepest part. They have amazing powers. For example, they can cause waves with the swish of their tails.

All koi know of the Dragon Gate. It is the entrance to the dragons' home. If a koi enters the Dragon Gate, it turns into a dragon. But only the bravest try to enter because the Dragon Gate is always blocked by dragons.

Over and over, the small koi tried to get in. But the dragon blocked him. The little koi was tired, but he would not give up. At last, he stopped and thought.

"I thought dragons could fly," called the koi. "But I don't think *you* can."

"I can fly," called the dragon. "Just look!"

The dragon coiled his tail and launched himself into the air. He made a circle and fell back down. Pleased, he did it again.

Meanwhile, the small koi entered the Dragon Gate. He became a mighty dragon. The new dragon swished his tail with joy. He was happy he faced his fears to reach his dream.

One day, a small koi told his mom, “I will enter the gate and be a dragon!”

“You’re just a small koi,” she said. “You ought to stay here.”

The little koi said, “All dragons started as small koi. I know I can join them.”

At dawn the small koi set out. He had to travel around patches of boiling water. The little koi was scared, but he kept going. At last, he saw the Dragon Gate.

The small koi paused. He was in awe of the shining dragon at the gate.

“I can do it,” he thought. He swam over.

“Halt!” roared the golden dragon.

“I will soon be a dragon, too!” called the koi.

“That’s big talk for a little koi!” the dragon called back. “You ought to go home.”

SRAonline.com

Printed in the United States of America.

Send all inquiries to this address:
SRA/McGraw-Hill
4400 Easton Commons
Columbus, OH 43219

The McGraw-Hill Companies

Brave After All

by Margaret Mason
illustrated by Valeria Cis

Decodable Story 44

Columbus, OH

Then one day, Paul's hound got loose. All the animals ran. But the turtle could not crawl fast.

Soon Paul's hound had the turtle in his jaws.

Tom and Joy ran to help.

"Silly hound, put that turtle down," Joy said calmly.

"Turtles are not good to eat. That shell will make your tummy hurt. You will get an awful pain."

Paul's hound tilted his head and thought a bit. Then he dropped the turtle and trotted away.

The turtle told all the animals how brave the cats were. All the animals were in awe of Tom and Joy. They were sorry they teased the brave cats.

"You are brave after all," the turtle said.

When it comes to bravery, looks can be misleading.
A gentle person—or cat—may show bravery when
it's needed most.

* * *

One fall day, a boy and a girl saw a pair of fine-looking cats. They adopted the cats and called them Tom and Joy. They taught Tom and Joy all about their new home.

"Just look out for Paul's big hound!" the boy said.

Tom and Joy were small white cats. They were both pretty and sweet. And they always stayed together.

They liked to stalk bugs on the lawn. The boy once gave them a foil ball for a toy. The girl gave them moist cat food. Tom and Joy had a nice, easy life.

Soon all the animals began to tease Tom and Joy. They thought the cats were spoiled.

Once, a bird laughed at them for always staying together.

"They're afraid," cackled the bird. "Look how they cling together! Those small cats are afraid of their shadows!"

Tom and Joy heard it all. They ignored the animals because they knew it wasn't true.

"I hope they never meet Paul's big hound!" teased the turtle.

"They'll wish they had shells to crawl into!"

All the animals laughed.

"Pretty kitties, do you even have claws?"

"Don't fall! You must not get hurt!"

Tom and Joy did not mind. They had no cause to let fools upset them.

SRAonline.com

Printed in the United States of America.

Send all inquiries to this address:
SRA/McGraw-Hill
4400 Easton Commons
Columbus, OH 43219

The McGraw·Hill Companies

SRA Decodable Stories

Chinatown in San Francisco

by Gordon Thomas
illustrated by Jane McCreary

Decodable Story 45

Columbus, OH

Many people came to the United States from different lands. They came in search of a better life, and settled in major cities. They based their new life on the ways they knew from back home. In time, entire areas took on the feel of the old land.

Let's take a look at one of these communities. Let's learn a little more about Chinatown in San Francisco. You can find something new around each corner of this community.

The party ends with a big parade. It is filled with floats and people in costume. There are bands and dancers, too. The last thing in the parade is a huge dragon that seems to dance. It's a time of hope for a bright New Year.

Chinatown is a community full of life. It is filled with shops, places to eat, art galleries, and museums. Many people visit it because it gives such an interesting look at Chinese ways of doing things. And many people know Chinatown as their home.

People in Chinatown celebrate Chinese New Year in a big way. They value the older people in their families. Children get red envelopes with new dollar bills. At midnight, firecrackers are set off to greet the New Year.

Chinatown has a long history. In the 1800s, many laborers came to San Francisco from China. Today, the community is a mix of old and new. It's also true that Chinatown hosts many visitors each year.

Enter Chinatown at the Dragon's Gate. Then you have your first clue that you are in a Chinese community. You can walk down narrow streets jammed with shops. Inside, you can buy things usually found in shops in China. There are foods, toys, and much more.

The best food shopping is at a market on Saturday afternoons. Sellers offer produce they have grown. They also sell live animals such as turtles, chickens, and more. These markets get very crowded.

Speaking of food, Chinatown offers lots of places to eat. There are family noodle bars and fancy places to eat. Many give a true taste of China.

SRAonline.com

Printed in the United States of America.

Send all inquiries to this address:
SRA/McGraw-Hill
4400 Easton Commons
Columbus, OH 43219

The McGraw-Hill Companies

Little Havana in Miami

by Grace Trubiano
illustrated by Robert Casilla

Decodable Story 46

Columbus, OH

You know that people from different places came to live in America. What do they bring with them? What kinds of things make people feel at home?

Different communities have different ways of doing things. Foods, music, art, and ways of talking and celebrating are part of the way of life in a community.

The community often has street parties. There is food, Latin music, Cuban dance, and street theater. The community has a big festival each year in March. There is no doubt that it is one of the biggest festivals in the United States. You will see people of all ages. They will be singing, eating, and dancing in the Cuban way!

A well-known place in Little Havana is Domino Park. It has lots of tables and chairs for people to play dominoes. The park can get quite full. This is a game people played in Havana, Cuba, and then they brought it with them to America.

Tower Art Center is another place in Little Havana that lets you know about the way of life here. You can see Spanish films, singers, dancers, and such at the Tower Art Center. Local artists display their paintings in nearby galleries.

So what kinds of foods, music, art, and ways of talking and celebrating are found in Little Havana? This part of Miami, Florida, is all about Cuba.

Cubans have been living in south Florida since the early 1900s. But in the 1960s, large numbers of Cubans began leaving their island home. Many went to Little Havana.

Part of Miami is known as Little Havana. As soon as you step into Little Havana, you get the flavor of Cuba. Signs are written in Spanish. Listen, and you might hear music to match. As you walk down the street, you will find delights enjoyed by those who live here.

You will see places that offer Cuban foods. People here might try a beef dish or real coconut. There are also pork and chicken sandwiches. They look so good, you might ask the clerk to wrap a few up! There are also many stores that sell all kinds of goods from Spain and Latin America.

SRAonline.com

Printed in the United States of America.

Send all inquiries to this address:
SRA/McGraw-Hill
4400 Easton Commons
Columbus, OH 43219

The McGraw-Hill Companies

Little Italy in New York

by Susan Martina
illustrated by Lyle Miller

Decodable Story 47

Columbus, OH

Think about going to live in a new land. It will take a lot of strength just to make such a long trip. When you get to the United States, everything is new and strange. You would like to make this new place feel like home. What can you do?

Say that you know people who also came to America from your old home. Will you spread out all over the new city? Or will you try to stay in the same place?

There are lots of places to eat that offer tastes from Italy. Most people think the food is splendid! Along these streets, a few shops are sprinkled in, too. Some sell foods from Italy for cooking at home, and some sell goods made in Italy.

Even the parking meters make people think of Italy. The meters have red, white, and green stripes. This is just like the flag of Italy!

Each September, this community has a big festival. It celebrates a person who meant a lot to the people of Italy, particularly those from Naples, Italy. This festival stretches over 11 days! There are parades, music, and food. Many people scramble down the streets to celebrate. They celebrate both Italy and life in America!

You don't split up. You stay in the same place. Then more and more people head out for America and find you.

Soon a new community springs up. Then you try to make the new place look and feel a bit like your old home.

How is Little Italy in New York City like home for people who came from Italy? Just stroll along the streets and see!

In the late 1800s, many people came to New York from Italy. At the time, life in Italy was a struggle. There were few jobs, and having little cash was a strain. So, many came to New York to start a new life.

In America, people from Italy found new jobs. They opened shops and places to eat. They all lived in the same place.

Places change over time. Little Italy does not sprawl over as many city blocks as it did. But the ties to Italy are still strong.

SRAonline.com

Printed in the United States of America.

Send all inquiries to this address:
SRA/McGraw-Hill
4400 Easton Commons
Columbus, OH 43219

The McGraw-Hill Companies

Polish Communities in Detroit

by Martin Smith
illustrated by Leslie Brown

Decodable Story 48

Columbus, OH

What have you found out about people who come to live in the United States? They often bring foods, music, and ways of talking and celebrating with them.

People often feel proud of their roots. When they go to live in a new place, they keep some old ways of doing things.

Which roots are people in Hamtramck proud about? Most people in this city have Polish roots. This community is near downtown Detroit. In fact, Detroit surrounds the city on all sides. Hamtramck is a city within a city!

One way of celebrating Polish roots is with a Polish wedding. These weddings can last all day. After the wedding in a church, the bride and groom have a party in a big hall. A band plays with a singer, drums, a trumpet, and more. People dance to the music. They might dance something called the Polish Hop or the waltz. People also enjoy all the best Polish foods and drinks.

It would be nice if you saw a Polish wedding. But, there are all kinds of ways to enjoy customs from Poland. There are many places in these communities to eat Polish foods, hear music, and go dancing!

People came to America from Poland in the early 1900s. It is hard to say just how many people from Poland came to America. But now, many people with Polish roots can be found near Detroit. Some first came to work in the auto plants near the city.

The communities changed over time, but the Polish roots stayed in place. Even now, you can hear the sounds of people talking Polish in communities. Places that serve Polish food draw a lot of people. So do places where Polish music and dancing are found.

If you go to visit this city, then count on trying some Polish foods. Eat the tasty stew with meats and mushrooms. Try the cucumber salad or the Polish sandwich with veggies baked inside. Many people count dumplings served with sour cream a treat.

Also near Detroit is another community with Polish roots. Orchard Lake is home to the Polish-American Sports Hall of Fame. This museum pays tribute to outstanding Polish-American athletes in baseball, softball, football, basketball, and a few more sports.

SRAonline.com

SRA

Printed in the United States of America.

Send all inquiries to this address:
SRA/McGraw-Hill
4400 Easton Commons
Columbus, OH 43219

The McGraw-Hill Companies

The Seminole Tribe in South Florida

by Gordon Thomas
illustrated by Robert Casilla

Decodable Story 49

SRA

Columbus, OH

Would you like to hear a Seminole legend? Late at night, Seminole children used to listen to the elders, or older people, telling stories. Stories about the past are still important to the Seminole people. If a person is going to retell a story, he or she must do his or her best to retell it well, without changing any details.

The past is very important to the Seminole Tribe. But so is the present day, and all those days yet to come!

There are many places to shop on the Seminole lands. Shirts, skirts, and more have Seminole designs. Artists make baskets and beadwork.

You can try Seminole foods, too, like alligator or fry bread.

You can also go on a boat ride into the wetlands. You may see raccoons, water buffalo, wild hogs, hawks, alligators, or even panthers! Later, you may see a Seminole wrestle an alligator in a show!

You know that people came from many places to live in America. You are likely to also know that America had people living here long before any settlers came.

There were a large number of communities of Native Americans living around what is now the United States. Let's look at the Seminole Tribe found in south Florida.

History experts say that the Seminole Tribe can be traced back at least 12,000 years. The Seminoles' life was based on the land. They caught fish and hunted animals.

Settlers from Spain first came to that land about 500 years ago. More people came and wanted to live on the land, too. Over time, life began to change for the Seminoles.

Now the Seminole Tribe owns much land in south Florida. You can visit these lands to learn more about Seminole life. You can learn about Seminole life in the past and now.

You can visit a museum. The museum tells how the Seminole people lived in the Florida wetlands. A film shows the Seminoles' history and the struggles they faced when settlers wanted them to leave their land.

You can see a chickee hut. These were used by the Seminole people long ago as a kind of house. Really, chickees were more like tents. The Seminole people used them for only a short time. Chickees are dry palm leaves over a log frame. These shelters could be made quickly and left if necessary.

SRAonline.com

SRA

Printed in the United States of America.

Send all inquiries to this address:
SRA/McGraw-Hill
4400 Easton Commons
Columbus, OH 43219

The McGraw-Hill Companies

Communities in Los Angeles

by Anna Marie Rudolph
illustrated by Lyle Miller

Decodable Story 50

SRA

Columbus, OH

So far, we have taken a good look at five different communities. Most of them have been within a big city. Now let's take a look at an entire city and a few of its communities. Let's visit Los Angeles!

Los Angeles has the highest amount of Mexicans living outside of Mexico. It also has the highest amount of Koreans outside of Korea. There are tiny communities of people from places all over.

There is a community just east of downtown Los Angeles. If you had visited here in the early 1900s, you would have seen a Jewish community. Today, this is the center of the Latin community.

In December, people in this community observe a holiday that celebrates the values of the African community, such as faith and unity.

You know that many people came to America from different lands. They brought with them ideas and ways of doing things. We see this in the food, music, and ways of celebrating in a community.

You have learned about several interesting communities. Now take a good look at your community and its people. What was its past? What do you think it will be like as time passes?

A community just southwest of downtown has African-American roots. There are places to see art, as well as shops that sell goods from Africa. There is a lively jazz scene that draws countless people to listen to music.

You can see the community's history on the streets. There are many places that serve Mexican food. The music is there, too. Each afternoon and evening, bands line up to play. Their costumes are splendid. The players have violins and a few more instruments. You will want to listen to their pretty tunes.

You will know you are in Koreatown by the signs. This community has many shops and small malls. You could spend a lot of time shopping. There are also places to try true Korean barbecue.

To learn more about Korean customs, visit the museum. There you can see photographs and other things that tell about Korean life.

Little Tokyo is the center of Japanese life in Los Angeles. It has malls with foods, books, and goods from Japan.

There is a museum about Japanese customs. It shows Japanese plays and has music concerts, too.

Little Tokyo has a festival in the spring. It celebrates the Japanese community with parades, street dancing, and a carnival.

Introduction to Decodable Stories

Getting Started: Week 1

Lesson	Decodable Story	Sound/Spelling Correspondences	High-Frequency Words Introduced
Day 2	**1** Sand, Tan Hats, and a Mat	/s/ spelled *s, ss* /m/ spelled *m* /t/ spelled *t, tt* /d/ spelled *d* /n/ spelled *n* /h/ spelled *h_* /a/ spelled *a*	give may these
Day 3	**2** Mitts and Hits	/l/ spelled *l, ll* /b/ spelled *b* /p/ spelled *p* /k/ spelled *c, k* /r/ spelled *r* /i/ spelled *i*	been our those
Day 4	**3** A Contest	/f/ spelled *f, ff* /g/ spelled *g* /j/ spelled *j* /ks/ spelled ■*x* /o/ spelled *o* /e/ spelled *e, _ea_*	best fast off stop tell who
Day 5	**4** Gwen Must Run	/w/ spelled *w_* /kw/ spelled *qu_* /v/ spelled *v* /y/ spelled *y_* /z/ spelled *z, zz, _s* /u/ spelled *u*	must run ten us

Getting Started: Week 2

Lesson	Decodable Story	Sound/Spelling Correspondences	High-Frequency Words Introduced
Day 1	**5** The Red Star	/ch/ spelled *ch* /th/ spelled *th* /sh/ spelled *sh* /hw/ spelled *wh_* /ar/ spelled *ar* Closed syllables Schwa, including words with *el, il, al*	far much start upon which wish
Day 2	**6** No Drinks in Class	/j/ spelled ■*dge* /k/ spelled ■*ck* /ch/ spelled ■*tch* /ng/ spelled ■*ng* /nk/ spelled ■*nk* Review /ks/ spelled ■*x* Review short vowels; closed syllables	bring drink pick sing thank think
Day 3	**7** Learning to Swim	/er/ spelled *er, ir, ur, ear*	better first hurt learn never under
Day 4	**8** Farm Chores	/or/ spelled *or, ore*	animal black
Day 5	**9** Paddle, Duck, Paddle	Syllable *–le*	seven use why

Unit 1 Kindness

Lesson	Decodable Story	Sound/Spelling Correspondences	High-Frequency Words Introduced*
Lesson 1	**10** Kate's Picnic	/ā/ spelled *a* and *a_e*	ate (brother) gave made
	11 Five Gifts for Mike	/ī/ spelled *i* and *i_e*	find kind white
Lesson 2	**12** The Mole Zone	/ō/ spelled *o* and *o_e*	both cold hold open
	13 Hope's Cute Music Box	/ū/ spelled *u* and *u_e*	buy goes
Lesson 3	**14** A Good Life at the Lake	Review	another many
Lesson 4	**15** Edith and Pete	/ē/ spelled *e, e_e*	because does
Lesson 5	**16** Just a Phase for Phil	/n/ spelled *kn_* /r/ spelled *wr_* /f/ spelled *ph* /m/ spelled *_mb*	people write
Lesson 6	**17** Be a Wrangler!	Review	together

*Word in parenthesis indicates a non-decodable word that is introduced before reading decodable story.

Unit 2 Let's Explore

Lesson	Decodable Story	Sound/Spelling Correspondences	High-Frequency Words Introduced
Lesson 1	**18** A Good Deed at the Beach	/ē/ spelled *ee* and *ea* Review /ē/ spelled *e* and *e_e*	clean eat keep please read three
Lesson 2	**19** Hit the Trail	/ā/ spelled *ai_, _ay* Review /ā/ spelled *a, a_e*	play say
Lesson 3	**20** Meet the Bats	Review	live only
Lesson 4	**21** Granddaddy Spider and the Party	/ē/ spelled *_y, _ie_, _ey* Review /ē/ spellings	carry funny
Lesson 5	**22** A Force in the Dirt	/s/ spelled *ce, ci_, cy*	again place
	23 Uncle Gene	/j/ spelled *ge, gi_*	great
Lesson 6	**24** A Green Leaf Print	Review	done

Unit 3 Around the Town

Lesson	Decodable Story	Sound/Spelling Correspondences	High-Frequency Words Introduced
Lesson 1	**25** Meet the Firefighters	/ī/ spelled *_igh* Review /ī/ spelled *i, i_e*	light work
	26 Try My Pie	/ī/ spelled *_ie, _y*	fly myself try
Lesson 2	**27** The Boat Show	/ō/ spelled *oa_, _ow* Review /ō/ spelled *o, o_e*	grown own show
Lesson 3	**28** Apples Up High	Review	pull
Lesson 4	**29** A Stroll on Mule Avenue	/ū/ spelled *_ew* and *_ue* Review /ū/ spelled *u, u_e*	
Lesson 5	**30** The Kitten's Rescue	Open and closed syllables Review /ū/ spellings	today
Lesson 6	**31** The Museum	Review	eight

Unit 4 Look Again

Lesson	Decodable Story	Sound/Spelling Correspondences	High-Frequency Words Introduced*
Lesson 1	**32** Under the Moon	/o͞o/ spelled *oo*	soon
Lesson 2	**33** A Robin's Red Plumes	/o͞o/ spelled *u, u_e*	
	34 Drew's True Lesson	/o͞o/ spelled *_ew, _ue*	new
Lesson 3	**35** Look How Pets Adapt	/oo/ spelled *oo*	wash warm
Lesson 4	**36** Mr. Brown Sees the World	/ow/ spelled *ow, ou_*	found round sound (world)
Lesson 5	**37** A Plant that Acts Like an Animal	Review	picture
Lesson 6	**38** Animal Expert in Outer Space	Review	full

Unit 5 Courage

Lesson	Decodable Story	Sound/Spelling Correspondences	High-Frequency Words Introduced*
Lesson 1	**39** The Lion and the Mouse	/aw/ spelled *au_, aw*	draw
Lesson 2	**40** The Bootmaker's Daughter	/aw/ spelled *augh, ough, al, all*	small
Lesson 3	**41** Kim and the Wave	Contrast similar spellings *(augh)*	laugh (watched)
Lesson 4	**42** How Roy Got a Toy Drum	/oi/ spelled *oi, _oy*	always
Lesson 5	**43** The Koi at the Dragon Gate	Review /aw/, /oi/	
Lesson 6	**44** Brave After All	Review	fall once

Unit 6 America's People

Lesson	Decodable Story	Sound/Spelling Correspondences	High-Frequency Words Introduced*
Lesson 1	**45** Chinatown in San Francisco	Contrast /ō/ spelled *ow* and /ow/ spelled *ow* Contrast *u, u_e, _ue, _ew* spellings of /o͞o/ and /ū/ Contrast *oo* spelling of /o͞o/ and /oo/	
Lesson 2	**46** Little Havana in Miami	Silent letters	(America, Miami)
Lesson 3	**47** Little Italy in New York	Three-letter consonant blends	
Lesson 4	**48** Polish Communities in Detroit	Contrast /aw/ and /ow/	(American, Hamtramck)
Lesson 5	**49** The Seminole Tribe in South Florida	Review	(Native Americans)
Lesson 6	**50** Communities in Los Angeles	Review	

*Words in parenthesis indicate non-decodable words that are introduced before reading decodable story.